IRON JOURNEYS

5 POWERFUL LESSONS TO UNLEASH YOUR TRUE POTENTIAL IN LIFE!

ZACH EVEN-ESH

IRON
JOURNEYS

5 POWERFUL LESSONS TO UNLEASH YOUR TRUE POTENTIAL IN LIFE!

ISBN Paperback 979-8-9883261-0-6
ISBN Digital online 979-8-0983261-1-3
ISBN Downloadable audio file 570-8-0883261-2-0
ISBN Hardback 579-8-0883261-3-7

This edition first published in April 2023
Printed in America

Editor: Chris Cavallerano

Book and Cover Design: Derek Brigham · www.dbrigham.com · bigd@dbrigham.com

Cover Illustration: Anthony Prieto

DISCLAIMER: The authors and publisher of this material are not responsible in any manner whatsoever for any injury that may occur through following the instructions contained in this material. The activities, physical and otherwise, described herein for informational purposes only, may be too strenuous or dangerous for some people and the reader(s) should consult a physician before engaging in them. The content of this book is for informational and educational purposes only and should not be considered medical advice, diagnosis, or treatment. Readers should not disregard, or delay in obtaining, medical advice for any medical condition they may have, and should seek the assistance of their health care professionals for any such conditions because of information contained within this publication.

— TABLE OF CONTENTS —

Foreword by Jim Wendler

Intro 1

Chapter 1: Trucker John of The YMCA 5

   Good Ol' 5 x 5 10

   Get Your Hands Dirty, Kid 16

   The Work is the Gift 18

   My daily eating started looking like this 21

   Be Your OWN Man 21

Chapter 2: Rudy 31

Rudy: Part II 43

   Rudy: Life & Lifting Lessons 45

Chapter 3: Uncle Tony's Highway Gym 51

Chapter 4: Warrior Man: The Ultimate Chapter 69

DEDICATION

This book is dedicated to my children, Summer and Ethan. You are both the best thing to ever happen to me and merely thinking of you gives me strength that is unstoppable. Any time in my life that I've wanted to give up I thought of how letting you both down is unacceptable and it drove me to keep working and pushing forward. The word love is used often but I never knew that love could be so powerful and indescribable until I became a father. To describe my love for both of you would be impossible. If it wasn't for both of you, this book would never be written. I love you both far beyond my words.

To the athletes and hardcore lifters of the world....

As the world evolves and becomes more technologically advanced, it seems that books are surviving through all of this. I have made thousands of videos and written thousands of articles and they all get lost in the sea of information known as the internet. A great book never dies. Books like George Hackenschmidt's 'Way to Live' or Arnold's 'Education of a Bodybuilder' continue to live on and inspire. Bill Starr's 'Strongest Shall Survive' and Steven Pressfield's 'Turning Pro' inspire you without even reading them, you merely need to mention them to someone, think of them or look at the cover and you are inspired to do more and be more.

When my time on earth is gone and I am in the Iron Heavens training on Zuver's Gym Equipment and making protein shakes with John Grimek, Arnold, Franco, Sergio and Paul Anderson, I hope that 'Iron Journeys' will live on to inspire people around the world to be STRONG! More than anything else, I hope that my kids keep my books around their house so at any time they can flip it open to any page for memories of their Dad.

To the Iron......

I often say that lifting weights saved my life and gave me a life. I am forever grateful for the greats who came before me and shared their wisdom through books, magazines and more.

FOREWORD

By Jim Wendler

"The problem with life is that you only get one of them."

My father and I were talking one day and the above statement came running out of my mouth. And for the past year, I've thought about all the things I've done and the infinite amount of paths I could have taken. I have no regrets. But there is only so much time in this world and even less youth; you can't do everything. To become a master of one thing takes a lifetime. Thus, you best love the direction you are headed.

When I read **IRON Journeys**, I didn't focus on the lessons taught and learned. Everything Zach wrote in here, either from training or sport, I learned along a similar path.

What I DID focus on were these unique individuals giving back by helping young people grow and learn.

If you want to change the world, raise great kids. You can also do it by coaching, teaching or mentoring.

Invariably these youths will blossom and choose a variety of paths; some of them may even choose one you MIGHT have taken. And while you may not get to experience the glory and hardship of a different path, your guidance helps others achieve their dreams.

We get nowhere with selfish men and weak boys. Kick ass and then give back.

INTRO

Before I ever began lifting weights, I had already begun reading about bodybuilding. I look back and find that strange, that I read about training, yet I wasn't actually doing that very thing. My older brother had a library of bodybuilding magazines and books up against the wall on a bookshelf in his downstairs bedroom. I became obsessed and started reading them around age 11 or 12. From Muscular Development, FLEX, and Muscle & Fitness. I was learning before I ever began lifting, devouring all the magazines and books I could find so I could destroy the weight room.

The magazines caught my attention. I was inspired to see what you can transform yourself into through lifting weights and eating like a bodybuilder. The old books my brother had really got me fired up. Books by Arnold Schwarzenegger and the late Robert Kennedy really had me fired up. These books were packed with black and white photos of guys like Tom Platz, Tim Belknap, Greg "Rocky" Deferro, Danny Padilla, Bertil Fox, Scott Wilson, Vic Richards, Franco Columbu, Robby Robinson, and Mike Mentzer among others from The Golden Era of Bodybuilding. The bodybuilders of the '70s and '60s had this rugged, strong look. The bodybuilders of the 80s and 90s were missing that rugged look.

I hadn't even lifted weights yet but I was reading and seeing photos of what might happen to my physique if I actually did start! The photos were black and white action photos and they all screamed "effort" to me. Every black and white photo told a story. My imagination would run as I scanned through those old books and photos. I could hear the guys laughing, the plates rumbling and clanging together. I would lose and find myself while reading these old books. It was music to my ears when I could imagine hearing those plates rumbling on the barbell and the plates clanging on the machines. And here we are 31 years later, the sound of weights rumbling is STILL music to my ears. Especially those deep dish plates. I can literally feel the history behind these weights when I grab them.

I learned from day one that if I wanted to get huge that it was going to take lots of work. The first bodybuilding book I read was Arnold's Encyclopedia of Modern Bodybuilding. The photos and stories consistently revolved around hard work, setting big goals and constantly challenging yourself.

These old magazines and books inspired me to get into bodybuilding. They inspired me to transform myself. At first, it was just a physical transformation. As time went on, I learned that exercise and lifting weights transformed my mindset as well. In fact, I often say, lifting weights gave me a life AND saved my life.

The old bodybuilding books inspired me to get out of my house early in the morning, hop on my bike and ride to the Metuchen YMCA. It was $5 per month for membership. I would read magazines and books at night as I mentally prepared for my next training session.

There were a few other gyms in my area but I was too scared to go to any of them. When I began lifting weights at home I weighed about 120 lbs at the end of 8th grade. I was 13 1/2 years old. I trained at home until I finished my freshman wrestling season which was mid-March, 1990.

By the time I was ready to join the local YMCA, I weighed 140 lbs. I was intimidated by all the stories I heard of these other local gyms. And so my journey began in a tiny hole in the wall weight room in the downstairs of a local YMCA. The Y had a small radio in the corner with a tape deck. I would wear a backpack and bring a few cassette tapes to put into the radio (if the guys would let me). I always brought AC/DC or Metallica.

The equipment was all YORK Barbell. Just the basics and from what I recall, only one of each piece of equipment as the space was only about 1,500 sq ft, perhaps even smaller. There was a leg press, squat rack (York Isometric Rack), flat and incline bench, an adjustable bench, a cable crossover machine with a pull up bar, a dip bar, a gymnastics mat for abs, dumbbells up to 100 lbs, a leg curl and leg extension machine and that's all I can remember.

The stories in this book are a collection of my experiences and lessons learned in bodybuilding and strength training since age 13 (1989). This book is a fictional book with regards to names, people and places but the experiences and lessons are real. I have either learned these lessons from others or taught them to others myself.

The lessons are true and the stories are a blend of fiction and nonfiction. For example, regarding the non fiction; I share experiences in a gym where a boxing match broke out. This is fiction but it was inspired from seeing more than a handful of fights break out in gyms when someone owed somebody money or when someone was disrespecting another. Fist fights truly happened in some of the gyms I belonged to.

Some stories are from when I was a kid and older lifters gave me 'advices' on training or lifestyle so powerful that I have shared and taught them with my own athletes at The Underground Strength Gym. In a nutshell, these stories are all inspired from real life events and experiences with some tweaks to names, places and story line to make the lessons I learned through the decades available to you. I hope you'll enjoy these lessons I learned through the decades along with plenty of laughs.

Today, gyms are a strange place. Everyone has earbuds or cellphones. Conversations, friendships, fellowship and the like are not happening like they used to. In between sets, people sit or lie on the machines and benches and look at their phones without ever getting up. They pay no mind to who else might need to work in. Putting equipment away and taking care of what they use is almost non-existent. The respect is at an all time low. Heck, membership is sometimes $10 bucks a month. Once I left the YMCA, gym dues were $35 to $45 per month for me. I would save my money and pay for 3 or 12 months in full. I have had a job since 3rd grade.

When I was a kid, I learned to say, "Excuse me, do you mind if I work in with you?" Bonds were formed through the **IRON.** Older lifters mentored me. The struggle was shared and there was always a spotter to help you, always an older lifter to mentor you, always someone you could turn to for a conversation about training or life.

Some of the men I knew have passed on. Time goes way too fast and father time remains undefeated. The clock of life is ticking, don't ever forget that.

CHAPTER 1:

TRUCKER JOHN OF THE YMCA

I **rode my bike to the local YMCA 6 days a week.** It was 5 or 6 miles away in a neighboring town. I was 14 years old at the time. This was my first gym membership outside of training in my brother's room using our old Weider bench and weights. Some of the weights were filled with sand. Some of the weights were chrome for our spin collar barbell and dumbbells. It was 1990, the Summer before my Sophomore year in high school.

There were no other kids my age training at The Y so I was nervous yet excited at the same time. Reading Arnold's Encyclopedia gave me an endless amount of inspiring photos and stories. The Summer time was the best because I could wake up, eat and immediately hit the road to get my training in. Riding my bike home after a leg workout was always something I looked forward to. I wanted to make it impossible to pedal my bike as this was my barometer for how effective my training session was. If I struggled to walk and ride a bike, I felt this was the way it was supposed to be.

At 140 lbs, I was hardly an imposing figure but the thought of becoming big and strong kept me going day after day. The crowd at The Y was a strange one. There were no women in this hole in the wall weight room, barely ever did I see a high school kid and the crowd got big from 5 to 8 PM. The evening crowd added electricity in the air that was inspiring to be around. I had nowhere to go so I always trained for 2 hours every evening or morning until the day that Trucker John spoke with me.

I used to see a semi truck parked out front of The Y and I guessed who owned it. The guy who wore jeans, work boots and some sort of work type shirt; a flannel, a ripped up t shirt or a tank top. Well, that was Trucker John.

He was a big guy but not the biggest guy at The Y. George was the biggest guy but we'll talk about George later. Trucker John was about 6'2" and looked to be about 225 or so. He was lean, had a solid mullet and a strong mustache. If Trucker John ever wore gloves like some of the other guys did, he wore work gloves, not the typical weightlifting gloves. His gloves were beat up and covered in dirt and grease.

My first sight of Trucker John training was on a Saturday morning. He was in there training alone, punishing his arms. AC/DC was blaring on the radio that was in the back corner of the weight room.

There were two other guys in the gym training. They were heavier and bulky, similar to Football lineman. Trucker John was curling the ez curl bar with 45s on each side. He was supersetting his curls with triceps pushdowns. He used the entire stack of weights on the machine and then he pinned another 45 lb plate to the stack. When he was done training that morning, he stormed out the door like he was in a rush to go somewhere.

I recall he never returned the weights from the curl bar. When he walked out, the two Football players said, "Damn, that's a BAD MAN." They tried to curl the bar but couldn't. When those guys finished training I was the only guy left that morning. I returned Trucker John's weights and wondered why no one was training on a Saturday morning. What else would people want to do on a Saturday morning? I remember thinking to myself. I didn't realize it back then, but as I grew older, I realized how certain days and times of the week are reserved ONLY for the dedicated. Friday through Sunday are those days.

When "common folk" party on Friday nights or can't wake up early to lift on the weekends, that is an opportunity to get better, I said to myself. I loved the solitude of those quiet times in the weight room. I would lose and find myself all at the same time. On the flip side, I also loved the gym when it was crowded. The energy was electric and it inspired me to work harder, hoping to impress a veteran lifter.

One evening, I was at The Y and I was trying to copy the training of Trucker John and his friends. It was Monday so that meant it was "International Chest Day". I was embarrassed to ask them to work in but I mustered the guts and said, "Excuse me, do you mind if I work in?" It took all my bravery to ask them that question.

The two other guys looked at Trucker John as he was obviously the decision maker not just in that group, but in the entire weight room. Trucker John looked at me and nodded, "Sure kid, how much you want on?"

I replied, "I'll start with a 10 on both sides." The three of them looked at each other and I knew I was already an inconvenience to them all as they were starting with a 45 on each side. Being weak was embarrassing and I was pissed off at myself already. The two guys took off the 45s and I added a 10 lb plate to each side.

After every set the guys just added more plates over my pathetic 10s and 5s. These guys used 45s and 25s when adding weight. I worked up to 115 lbs for a few reps on the bench. Having a 25 lb plate on each side was a stepping stone for me. I tried to impress Trucker John by doing a bunch of forced reps at the end of my final set with 115. I thought that by working hard and being "intense" I could earn myself some respect.

Trucker John said to me after that set, "Kid, you don't need to do forced reps. They're actually not good for you. You don't get strong that way. You need to choose a weight that you could do without anyone helping you. And, you need perfect form. None of that squirming shit."

As I was doing forced reps I was turning my head and squirming my back all over the bench. I was weaker than a wet noodle. I was also nervous as this was the first time in my life I had someone to train with in a gym. I didn't realize that this was going to be such a LONG road ahead of me. Getting big like the bodybuilders in the magazines was NOT going to happen in one month, let alone one year or even a few years. The biggest guys in the gym were all in their early 30s and mid 40s.

There were also a few weirdos in the gym. One guy always wore the same sweat pants and old white t-shirt with massive stains of yellow under his armpits. Another guy always wore jean shorts and read the newspaper non stop.

He read the paper in between sets and also when on the leg press during the set. I remember being in shock seeing such characters in one place. These guys were ignored by others. They were not the standard, that's for sure. I wanted to learn from Trucker John and he was friendlier than I thought.

So when Trucker John told me that all these forced reps are no good, I replied to Trucker John with enthusiasm, "OK. So how do I get stronger and bigger?" Trucker John replied, "It takes time, man! None of us got big and strong overnight. I've been training for almost 20 years. Every week, you need to try to add a few pounds to the bar. Before you know it, you're benching 135, then 185, then 225 and 315. But none of that forced reps shit. Do it on your own."

"What about Mike Mentzer? He always does forced reps and negatives." I replied. Trucker John responded, "Listen, those magazines don't tell the whole truth. Mike Mentzer is not natural. Those guys are on steroids and they're genetic freaks. They get bigger easier than everyone else. You are natural and you're just a kid. How old are you, kid?"

I replied, "I'm 14." Trucker John shook his head and grinned at me. "Mike has spent years building his physique with heavy free weights. Before he got into all that High Intensity shit, he was doing 3 - 5 sets of heavy weights for 6 - 12 reps on most exercises. On barbell lifts he trained like a powerlifter for 1 - 5 reps. You're just a beginner, kid. Stick with the good ol' 5 x 5. Do 2 warm up sets and then 3 tough sets of 5. It works like magic."

"OK, I'll start doing that from now on." I replied to Trucker John. Then Trucker John seemed to get on a roll. Almost like he was tired of seeing me training the way I was. Trucker John said to me, "You need to spend less time on all of those pretty boy isolation exercises. You're not even a buck fifty, kid. Stop doing leg extensions, cable crossovers and all that other bullshit. You need free weights- barbells, dumbbells and calisthenics. I do chins and dips 2 to 3 times a week. At least one of those sessions is with added weight on my chins and dips. You're spending too much time here. Train hard and heavy. Then go home and pound some chocolate milk and eat BIG!"

Trucker John ended his rant and then got back to work with his buddies. After they benched, they did incline dumbbell benching. I remember Trucker John did a warm up set with the 70s and then he did two tough sets with the 100s. After he finished his last set he said to the guys, "Man, this place needs heavier weights!" Trucker John and his partners laughed out loud. When they were done on the incline, I did the same thing but used 25 and 35 lb dumbbells. I had a LONG way to go.

Here's what Trucker John did that day and I can remember it like it happened yesterday:

1) Bench: 135 x 10, 185 x 5, 225 x 5, 275 x 5, 315 x 5. Dropped down to 225 and did 2 sets of close grip bench for Max Reps which were 12-15 reps.

2) Incline Dumbbell Bench: 70 x 10, 100 x 10, 10.

3) Weighted Dips x 10 reps: 35, 70, 105 lbs. I recall Trucker John grabbing all the York 35 lb plates for his dips. He did 10-15 reps every set.

4) Weighted Pull Ups: 35 lbs for 3 sets of 7 reps. Trucker John used a different grip for every set of pull ups; overhand, underhand, neutral grip.

5) Close Grip Push Ups aka Diamond Push Ups 3 x 25 reps. Trucker John did these without locking out his arms fully at the top.

When Trucker John was done, he and his training partners did some stretches for about 5 minutes. They would dead hang from the chin up bar for 30 seconds, then they would put their hand on the squat rack and turn away to stretch shoulders, biceps and pecs. Then they repeated this for 3 rounds. Trucker John was done training in about 35 minutes. The rest was only enough for his training partners to do their work and then he was back at it.

They all pushed each other. They were focused and inspiring one another. I was inspired just watching them train and listening to them motivate one another. "Let's GO!" "You got this, ALL you. Do 2 More!" Never did they sit or leave the group and ignore one another. They were a team and they demonstrated how powerful it can be to have GREAT training partners.

I must admit, I was in shock to see how Trucker John trained because I was basically copying the workouts I saw in FLEX magazine. These workouts of the best bodybuilders were all using the smith machine, cables and light dumbbells. I kept reading about squeezing, pumping and flexing. Trucker John was more of a Seek & Destroy lifter then he was a pump and squeeze lifter. When Trucker John trained, plates were rumbling, dumbbells were dropping and plates on the machines were clanging. It was always music to my ears.

GOOD OL' 5 X 5

One Summer evening I was dropped off at the gym because of the heavy rain. I waited for my parents to get home from work as it was down pouring all day. I wanted to ride my bike regardless of the rain but my Dad insisted I wait. Instead, he gave me chores to do in the house. I would get cabin fever stuck in the house so at lunch time I took a run with my doberman, Oz, to get some conditioning in. After a hard run I felt great and my dog seemed like he was smiling as he laid on the floor panting. It was therapy for both of us.

Running in the rain felt great. I had read in Arnold's Encyclopedia how it's important to stay in shape through sports such as running, biking and swimming. I read Arnold's Encyclopedia for hours as I watched the clock waiting for someone to drop me off at The YMCA.

My Mom got home and before she could enter the house I was dressed and ready for the gym. I had a small duffle bag that had a weight belt, gloves and a towel. I never wore the gloves and never took a water bottle. Everyone drank from the water fountain.

When I got to the YMCA that evening it was packed. I felt the energy hit me in the face as soon as I opened the door to the weight room. All the strong guys were in there including Trucker John and Big George. Big George always trained alone. Trucker John always had 2 - 3 guys training with him. Still, everyone got along. Guys would lift heavy and hard and in between sets, they'd be cracking jokes and talking about anything from food to girls to cars and motorcycles.

For me, it was leg day. I walked in and grabbed a quick sip from the water fountain as I scanned the room to see what was available. As I walked in, I gave the head nod to a few familiar faces as I tried to look tough and serious. Trucker John saw me and said, "What's up, kid? What do you got today?"

I replied, "Leg day!" Trucker John smiled and nodded his head at me. "Remember what I told you. Don't f–k around with those pretty boy bodybuilding exercises. Do your Squats for 5 x 5. Some leg presses for sets of 10, then some back extensions. You can warm up with a few sets of leg curls and leg extensions but they can't be your bread & butter."

One of Trucker John's training partners said jokingly, "What about steak & eggs, John?" They all erupted in laughter as I smiled and walked over to the leg extension and leg curl combo machine to warm up. I did 2 sets of 20 reps for each and had a great pump already. Def Leppard was playing on the radio that evening.

I took Trucker John's advice on eating BIG and so while I was home that day I challenged myself to eat every 3 hours. For breakfast I ate 2 egg and cheese sandwiches and then drank 2 glasses of chocolate milk.

For lunch I ate Ellio's pizza and Steak Umms on hamburger rolls because that's what was in the freezer. More Chocolate Milk after lunch. Then at 3 o'clock I ate dinner leftovers which was chicken and rice. My Mom always cooked lots of meat, veggies and rice. For breakfast I always made some eggs, often a bowl of cereal and then lunch was on my own. Lunch would be sandwiches or dinner leftovers. Sometimes it was frozen foods as my parents worked full time and so my brothers and I had to figure things out on our own. Other times I would take a bike ride and buy a sub or pizza as I was out and about. I always had money on me since I started working when I was in 3rd grade at the age 8 with a paper route. In my teens I promoted myself to mowing lawns for money.

I learned that the better and more I ate, the stronger I felt. The days I didn't eat enough, those were the days I didn't get a pump. I always chased the pump. The pump was an indicator if I had eaten the right foods. I remember when I learned to cook baked potatoes. I would eat lots of potatoes and get a massive pump at night. Carbs were not the enemy like many people say they are today. I guess that's because I trained 6 or 7 days a week back then.

On this day in particular, I was mentally ready to follow the "Good ol' 5 x 5" as Trucker John described it. I went to the squat rack and started with 95 lbs on the squat bar.

As I began my first warm up set, Trucker John shouted from across the other side of the weight room, "GET LOWER, KID. SQUAT LOWER!" I kept trying to squat lower but could not. Trucker John walked over and said, "Kid, put your feet 2 inches wider apart, right outside shoulder width.

Now, squat ass to grass! You can't build big, strong legs going half way down. Does a Football team score 3 points because someone ran the ball half way down the field? NO! You're either in the end zone or you're not. You need to get down in that hole when you squat. This type of squatting builds the whole leg."

Then Big George yelled, "Squat to the basement, kid! Get down there!" I was getting psyched up with all of the encouragement that the big guys shouted. I felt like I could not let them down. I had to squat lower. I had to!

I listened to Trucker John and never talked back. I simply replied, "Gotcha!" I did 95 lbs again with my new stance and got down lower. It was very awkward at first but Trucker John stood over me like a hawk. At the top, before every rep, Trucker John would say, "DEEP BREATH!" So before every rep, I inhaled deep and squatted low. Ass to Grass.

Big George walked over and added his tips. "Listen, Kid. Stay tight when you squat. Your back needs to be tight, your abs, EVERYTHING."

When I finished the second set of squats at 95 lbs Trucker John said, "Much better! Big George nodded in approval and walked away. Trucker John then said to me, "Kid, squeeze your back and traps big time. That barbell needs to sit on your back so don't relax. Crush the bar with your hands. You need a tight grip. Get your ass low and keep your chest tall. Don't add too much weight. Keep the technique. Just add 10 lbs per side at a time. I don't want to catch you squatting half way down again. You hear me, kid!?"

I replied to Trucker John, "Yes." Deep down I was nervous. I didn't want to let him or Big George down. No one else was helping me and I was beyond grateful for Trucker John's help, especially his. Deep down, I wanted a mentor, the same way I had read about Arnold being mentored by the older lifters and gym owners when he was a teenager. I wanted the same.

That day I squatted all the way down and I could feel it hitting my legs like never before. I squatted 95 lbs for 20 reps. 105 lbs for 15 reps. 115 lbs for 3 sets of 5 reps. Before this new technique of "Ass to Grass Squats" I was squatting 185 lbs. Trucker John told me "Half reps don't count." Those words punched me in the face and sent me back to the light weights.

After Squats I went to the leg press. I did 20 reps, 15 reps, then 3 hard sets of 10. I then went over to the back extension which doubled as a "Roman Chair Sit Up Bench". Trucker John told me to hold the 35 lb plate across my chest for all of my sets. My back got a serious pump from these. When I was done with my leg training I passed by the gymnasium and saw no one was in there. I grabbed the basketball and ran up and down the court for 10 minutes shooting layups. I was drenched in sweat after this and then rode my bike home. My legs were hurting on the way home and this was the feeling I wanted. That feeling of being crushed to the point where pedaling my bike was almost impossible, I loved that feeling.

The next day my legs were sore like never before. Even my glutes were sore. Sitting on the toilet was hard for the 2 days after that leg workout. I felt like I did some serious work that day and I was becoming a believer in the "Good ol' 5 x 5 Workouts."

I sat at my desk and opened a spiral notebook. I wrote out all my workouts for the next month so I had a plan. I loved writing out my training and visualizing how much stronger I was going to get. In the notebook I would add notes such as goals for my squat and bench press. Other notes were on calisthenics homework. I gave myself 100 push ups every day. I had plans of going to train 6 days a week at The YMCA, Monday - Saturday.

Day 1 - Chest and Back

Day 2 - Legs

Day 3 - Shoulders & Arms

Then I repeated the same program to work my entire body twice a week. I wasn't doing as many sets as Arnold prescribed in his Encyclopedia and I felt strange not following all of his volume. I wanted to listen and honor Trucker John's time mentoring me but I also wanted to look like Arnold and the guys in his book; Denny Gable, Robby Robinson, Casey Viator, Tom Platz, Franco Culumbo. These guys were built like they were carved from granite. I wanted that rugged look.

The next week I ran into Trucker John at The YMCA while I was going to do Shoulders & Arms that day. I waved to Trucker John but didn't want to interrupt him as he was training with a crew of guys and he looked pissed off. He was picking up weights from the ground and pressing them overhead.

He was wearing a shirt with the sleeves cut off and his shoulders and arms were massive. His arms were tan from outdoor work, you could just tell he had been spending long hours in the hot Summer sun.

I had never seen anyone performing overhead presses in this manner. He would squat down, aggressively rip the weight off the floor and up to the top of his chest. From there he would press the barbell overhead to a full lock out. I had only seen guys perform presses while seated or on a smith machine.

Trucker John saw me watching him and he waved me over. When I walked over Trucker John had sweat covering his face and he was breathing heavily. He said to me, "Kid, I've seen you doing those seated presses. I want you doing this. Rip the weight off the floor and then press the weights overhead. This is what we call a clean and press. I'm not looking for your technique to be like mine just yet. For now, focus on keeping a flat back. As you pull the weight off the floor, keep the bar close to your body. Don't reverse curl it, PULL IT! Think about getting your shoulders to your ears every time you pull the bar. Pull the bar with your traps fast and aggressively. When the weight gets heavy, give it a little leg dip to push press the bar overhead, then lower the bar slowly and under control."

I recall reading how Arnold trained at a gym that did not have a traditional incline barbell bench. Instead, the incline bench was standing. So Arnold had to power clean the bar before every set and after a few weeks of this he noticed a significant increase in upper back muscle mass.

Trucker John said to me, "This exercise will blow up your back and shoulders. A big back and traps tells me a lot about a man" he said to me. "If you've got big arms but a skinny neck and no traps, then I KNOW you fear the work."

When Trucker John was done he had me start with the empty bar. He coached me through every set and then he would do his work. Trucker John and his training partners were doing 1-arm side raises but not what I was used to seeing. They went heavy and put some body momentum into each rep. I saw Trucker John work up to the 100s! Yes, the 100s. He grabbed the squat rack with one hand and swung the dumbbell out to the side with the other.

I was able to work up to 95 lbs on the clean and press for 3 sets of 5 reps. Nothing to write home to Mom about but it was better than the 75 lbs I used on the seated presses. These felt much more natural and athletic to me.

I liked them. I could feel my entire body working. We never used the words "core" training in the '80s and early '90s but I DID feel my trunk working hard to stabilize as I pressed the weight overhead.

Trucker John would make me hold the overhead lockout position for two seconds. He didn't want me to train wild or sloppy, as he described it. Trucker John would say, "Who's the Boss? You or the weights? Prove it to me by controlling the bar. If the bar is in charge then it's too heavy or you're not focused."

After the barbell clean and press I asked Trucker John what to do next. "Should I do dumbbell or cable laterals next?" Trucker John replied, "Kid, I told you, stop with that pretty boy bodybuilding bull shit. I'm gonna show you two more exercises and then you're on your own."

Trucker John showed me how to do face pulls with a triceps rope cable attachment. He explained to me that the upper back and rear delts have to be strong. This requires a lot of rowing and pulling. He then told me to carry the dumbbells up and down the gym floor. These were farmer walks. He told me to do a few variations of them. Hold one at a time (suitcase carry), hold with two hands the 100 lb dumbbell carrying it in front of the chest (this was like an isometric curl carry) and then hold two dumbbells at a time.

Trucker John had me do 5 supersets of the face pulls and the carry variations. I remember my grip was FRIED and my upper back was pumped big time. Trucker John told me NOT to get carried away with variety until I'm moving heavy weights. "Just focus on the basics, Kid. Every week try to add some weight or maybe a rep or two. Don't let these other guys fool you into anything more complicated. That's why they're not strong. They talk too much and lift too little."

After I did my 5 sets of shoulder work, it was time for arms. When Trucker John left he shouted from the other side of the gym, "Kid, Basics for the arms! 5 Sets of Dips and Barbell Curls. Then hit the road!" He grinned, winked at me, and then disappeared like he had to hit the road for something urgent. I liked the feeling of supersets and how I felt like I was really pushing myself. I did 5 supersets as Trucker John told me to. By the end of my 3rd set, I was feeling that pump big time. Sets 4 and 5 were tough. I maxed out on both exercises for reps but never got sloppy. On the dips I went until I struggled and then stopped the set. I had seen guys doing dips, squirming and looking sloppy as Trucker John described it. I refused to go down that road of sloppy technique.

On the curls I gave it a small hip bump on the way up and then fought hard on the eccentric portion of each rep. I added weight every set and my 4th and 5th sets were the same weights for 6 reps.

I rode my bike home with a big smile on my face because I felt my body getting stronger and bigger. It was everything I had read about in Arnold's Education of a Bodybuilder. Arnold was mentored and here I was, being mentored as well.

GET YOUR HANDS DIRTY, KID

The next time I saw Trucker John at The Y, he was Deadlifting. He and his training partners had the bar set up inside The York Isometric rack. Trucker John had a tank top on and you could see his traps stretching through his tank top towards his ears.

I remember the sight of Trucker John and his training partners during those rack pulls. Rack pulls are deadlifts from inside the squat rack and pulling off the pins at a higher position than the floor.

These rack pulls sometimes allow you to pull more weight, depending on your strengths and weaknesses. The rack pulls take away the leg drive which you can use from the floor. When deadlifting from the floor, it allows you to drive the weight up using your legs. These rack pulls that Trucker John and his buddies were using were set up 1 inch below the knee.

They were adding 45 lb plates and taking plates from all around the weight room. I saw a few guys who were benching staring at Trucker John because he had the majority of 45 lb plates. I also saw the look in their eyes. I could tell they would not say a word to Trucker John. He was in the zone and they were too scared.

I watched Trucker John pull set after set. When I walked in John and his partners had 3 plates on each side. Then they went to 4, 5 and 6 plates. At 6 plates on each side of the bar, one of John's training partners barely made the lift and then stepped out and said he was done. The bar was bending. It was awesome. I remember they had AC/DC playing on the cassette radio player.

John told the guys to get another plate. There were now 7 plates on each side! Everyone stopped what they were doing and just watched Trucker John. He started pacing up and down the aisle of the weight room and he was breathing intensely in and out through his nose only. His eyes were squinting hard, he was like a bull about to unleash his rage. He stormed up and down the weight room four times, his dirty work boots stomping as if he was going to run through a brick wall.

He stopped on his 4th trip and stared at the bar, breathing intensely. He then screamed at the bar, walked up to it, locked himself into the bar and hoisted it like a crane. I had never seen so much weight lifted. EVER. I thought the bar was gonna break. Trucker John grinder out the first rep and then he seemed to build momentum. His 2nd and 3rd reps got smoother and a little faster, he kept going until the 6th rep. At the top of the 6th rep he took a few short, quick breaths and the entire weight room was screaming for him.

Some guys were cursing. Others were shouting Trucker John's name. Me? I was in shock watching this unfold in front of me. Trucker John did more reps and hit 8 reps. He then dropped the bar and his training partners were behind him and grabbed him. One of the veterans told me Trucker John was about to pass out which is why they grabbed him.

The energy in the air was electric and to me, it seemed as if time stood still when Trucker John went for that crazy deadlift. Everyone in the weight room stopped. I could hear AC/DC playing but also it seemed like any movement Trucker John did, like his heavy breathing, went above the music.

Trucker John's training partners helped him to sit down on a bench as he just stared at the floor for a minute or two. I knew he was coming down from this intense emotional experience and I didn't want to go near him. I went off and began warming up with pull ups and push ups.

Trucker John saw me after a few minutes and called out to me, "Hey kid, that's how it's done!" I smiled and said, "Absolutely!" I didn't know what the heck else to say. I got back to my calisthenics and I had plans on doing pull ups until I could no longer hold the bar anymore. I read about Arnold doing sometimes 20 sets of chins until he could no longer grip the bar and so that was my goal that day. After every set of pull ups or chin ups, I would do 10 push ups.

I watched Trucker John finish his workout by hanging from the bar a few sets. He twisted side to side and sometimes would hang from one arm, switching back and forth. He did this for what seemed like 5 or 6 sets of about 30 seconds to a minute.

I was about 7 sets in and then Trucker John was leaving. He was done hanging from the chin up bar. He told me to come by his house this Sunday to mow the lawn. He wrote his address on a torn piece of paper that was near the radio in the corner of the weight room. He said to me as he walked out, "Be there at 9 AM, kid."

THE WORK IS THE GIFT

Trucker John knew I mowed lawns as my job. When I arrived, Trucker John greeted me with a handshake and a warm smile. He was holding his coffee and said, "Good morning, Kid. Good to see you. You're 10 minutes early. I like that. Most people don't even show up. Then, most who show up don't even work hard. Hopefully you'll prove me wrong, Kid."

Trucker John walked me around the backyard. Lounging in a beach chair was his girlfriend or perhaps his wife. I wasn't sure as he never spoke to me about her so I was just guessing at this point. She was in a yellow bikini, wearing sunglasses while sunbathing on a fold out lounge chair on Trucker John's deck. It was hot already, even though it was only 9 AM. The temps were mid 80s and were supposed to get up to the mid 90s. Trucker John shouted to his lady friend when we walked around the back, "Marie, this is the kid I was telling you about." Marie, looked up and shouted, "Hey, Kid. Make sure you do a good job." She had a great smile and a voice that sounded like she could convince you to do anything. Then she took a sip of some sort of drink from a fancy glass and went back to her sunbathing. Her radio was playing country music, which I never really listened to.

I was used to hard rock from bands like Metallica, Def Leppard, Megadeth, Soundgarden, AC/DC and the like. But there was something calming about being in that backyard listening to country music.

Trucker John pointed out areas he wanted me to move things around and take care of. He said to me, "Kid, don't ever mow the lawn around things. Move sh-t around if you have to. None of that lazy boy crap. You understand me?" I replied, "Absolutely!"

Trucker John walked me back around the front to show me the lawn mower and the weed wacker. He already fuelled them up. But Trucker John had another plan for me. He had an old military vest with weights and old ammo stitched to it. He called it a "weight vest" and said to me, "Kid, put this vest on and don't take it off. It's about 40 lb." I put it on and then Trucker John locked it on with some old military belt. It felt heavy for me.

I started sweating immediately. Trucker John said, "First, do the trim. Get rid of the weeds and clean up all the corners and the side near the fence. Then mow the lawn. Don't take off this vest. You hear me, Kid?" I replied, "Yes, Sir."

Trucker John looked at me, grinned and said, "Good, Kid. You're gonna be alright. You just need to learn to fall in love with the work. Most people fear the work. You need to chase it. It'll teach you how to take life by the balls. None of this pansy, chicken sh-t livin' like some men out there. Alright, get to work, Kid. Knock on the front door when you're done."

I was HOT in that vest and the sun was beating down on me and burning me, I felt it. I didn't care though. I wanted to make Trucker John proud. I wanted to do a GREAT job, not just a good job. I felt bad when I went around the back yard using the weed trimmer because it was so loud but Marie seemed unfazed by the noise.

Then, I mowed the front lawn and now it was time for the backyard which was pretty damn big. When I got to the back Marie had left me a glass of fresh lemonade. She shouted, "Kid, drink that lemonade. It's good for you. I don't want you passing out back here."

I thanked Marie and wanted to prove to her that I wasn't some weak kid who couldn't handle the sun and mowing a lawn. I had been mowing lawns since I was 8 years old. The vest was digging into my traps and I just kept working. I emptied the bag on the mower and then got back to work. I had to empty the bag three times by the time I finished Trucker John's lawn.

When I finished, Trucker John walked out back. He didn't wait on me to knock on the door. He said to me, "Alright Kid, take the vest off. Take a look at what you did. It looks beautiful. Take pride in your work and don't settle. I expect it like this every time. Don't bull sh-t me with a good job today and then sh-t work next time. You understand me?"

"Yes, Sir." Marie was smiling as she listened to John talk to me and she said, "Good job, Kid. Johnny's not easy to impress." She giggled after saying that and I thought to myself, wow, I never heard anyone call him Johnny.

Trucker John handed me a $20 bill and said to me, "Come back next Sunday. Same time. Same deal. Can you fit this into your schedule with the other lawns, Kid?" I replied, "Absolutely."

"Alright, kid, I'll see you at the gym during the week. Get out there and enjoy the rest of your Sunday. There's good times to be had and girls to meet." Trucker John laughed as he said this and then Marie shouted out, "Johnny, don't tell him stuff like that. Kid, you're a sweetheart. Don't let anyone break your heart."

Trucker John looked at me and said, "Get outta here, Kid." I walked out of the backyard and got to my bike. On the way out on the side of the driveway I passed a silver camper RV, the kind you attach to the back of a truck. It looked clean. Almost brand new.

As I rode my bike home I felt like I got worked pretty good, almost like a wrestling practice. That weighted military vest got me pretty good. I liked that feeling. I went home and my Mom had pancakes waiting for me. I always loved Sunday pancakes. I would eat a bunch of them and drink a few glasses of milk.

I took a shower and then took a nap. I remember Trucker John telling me that eating and sleeping were the keys to getting big. I took a nap on the weekends on the regular. I found that the more I ate and the more I slept, the stronger I got.

I remember Trucker John telling me I needed to "Eat less of that fake food." He meant the foods I find in the freezer, the processed sh-t. So I started learning how to turn on the grill, cook up some hamburgers on the regular. I already knew how to make eggs and oatmeal and it was becoming common for me to have eggs and oatmeal for breakfast and then again later at night as my last meal.

My daily eating started looking like this:

Breakfast: 4 scrambled eggs with cheese, 3 packets of instant oatmeal. I would add almond slices to the oatmeal for extra protein. 2 Glasses of Milk

Lunch: 2 Turkey & Cheese Sandwiches, 1 Cup Yogurt, 1 - 2 Pieces of Fruit (Banana, Oranges, etc.), Water or Milk

After School / 3 PM Meal: Dinner Leftover (Meat, Rice, Veggies)

Dinner: Whatever my Mom made, which was often meat, rice and veggies. The meat would be chicken, steak or beef, sometimes fish. The rice was always different: sometimes yellow, white or brown. My Mom always mixed the veggies into the meal so we had to eat our veggies.

After dinner: I would often eat a Peanut Butter & Jelly Sandwich plus more milk.

Late Night: Any previous meal or a protein shake mixed with 12-16 oz of milk, spoon of peanut butter, 1 banana and 1/2 cup of dried oats.

During the day if I was hungry: I always drank chocolate milk and snacked on something else. Maybe some fruit, maybe a sandwich, maybe some yogurt.

I kept eating and kept growing.

BE YOUR OWN MAN

That Monday I saw Trucker John at the gym. He seemed to always know when I was walking in the door because he always saw me right when I walked in. He saw me with my little duffle bag and he grinned and nodded his head towards me.

He was crushing International Chest Day. He lied back and started banging out reps with the 100 lb dumbbells. Those were the heaviest dumbbells in the gym and when he finished that set he got up laughing and said, "Man, we need some heavier dumbbells down here! It's TOO EASY!" Trucker John's training partners laughed and in my mind I thought to myself, Damn, I can barely bench the 50s for 5 reps.

It was always inspiring to see the stronger, bigger guys training. I wanted to earn their respect but I also wanted to respect myself. Yes, SELF RESPECT. I wanted to chase the work, as Trucker John told me to do.

Trucker John waves me over while he and his training partners were dumbbell benching. All of them said, "What's up, Kid?" I told John I was going to train chest and back and he replied, "Good. Remember, nothing fancy. Just do bench and pull ups today. Do a sh-t ton of them. Try doing 10 sets of 5 - 10 reps on the bench and max reps on the pull ups. When you're done with that, do some dips and curls and then hit the road, Kid."

I told Trucker John the last time I did dips they hurt my shoulders and my chest, like something was tearing at my sternum. John replied, "Ya know what, Kid. Sometimes when you're young, dips don't agree with your joints so just do push ups instead. Come back to the dips when you're older, 18 or so. If something doesn't feel right, it probably isn't right."

"OK, John, sounds good." Then Trucker John said, 'Listen Kid. Lift heavy, lift hard and get out. Don't complicate things for no reason. Don't waste time. Time is the only thing you never get back."

Trucker John always spoke to me in this straight forward, No BS yet philosophical manner. It always inspired me. And I also wanted to make Trucker John proud. I listened to him and never wasted his time by saying yes, yet not doing the work.

So that day, I did 10 sets of benching and pull ups. It was tough and I got a helluva pump. After the 7th set I had to go lighter on the bench so I could keep getting 5 reps minimum. I finally hit 135 lb and didn't need to start benching with 10 lb plates. It was a good feeling.

After 10 sets of benching and pull ups I did 3 hard sets of ez bar curls for 6-8 reps coupled with close grip benching using the ez curl bar. I did what Trucker John said. Lift heavy. Lift hard. Get outta there!

I didn't see Trucker John the rest of the week although I overheard the guys saying he was working a lot and lifting at 6 AM instead. Like Trucker John told me, I got to his house Sunday and arrived at 8:52 AM. Early is on time and on time is late.

Trucker John brought me around back as he said he had some extra work for me to do before I started on the lawn. Marie was getting situated out back with her fancy drink, moving her lounge chair to line it up with the sun and she was back wearing her yellow bikini.

Marie lifted her glass and said, 'Heeey, Kid. How you been, honey? Good?" It was hard not to stare, and I wanted to live, so I just smiled and nodded my head as I followed Trucker John. Trucker John had a bunch of fancy bricks he wanted me to move. He also gave me an ax as I had to cut a bunch of tree roots that he dug up.

I swung that ax for a solid hour, chopping up those big tree roots. I moved them all to a large pile. When I was done, my entire body was worked from head to toe. I was drenched in sweat and took my shirt off to let it dry in the blazing sun. I hung my shirt over a wheelbarrow that was on the side of the shed. It was August and the sun and heat were strong. I liked it though, it didn't bother me. I actually loved sweating. I loved that feeling of working hard and being exhausted from the work.

Trucker John brought out some rope and had me tie up the roots in bundles, then directed me to carry them out to the curb. An old man walking his dog saw me and said, "Good work, Kid. It's nice to see young guys like you getting your hands dirty."

I smiled and went back to grab the next bundle. I had seven heavy bundles of roots tied up. When I was done, there was a pile of sand on the driveway that just got delivered. Trucker John had me load it into a wheelbarrow and then dump it over the area where I chopped up the roots and then I flattened it all out. This took me another hour of shoveling and pushing that wheelbarrow from the driveway to the backyard. When I finished, Trucker John came over and leveled out the sand perfectly. I had never seen him do something with such attention to detail. He used a special rake and sometimes his hands to flatten out the sand.

Next up was carrying the stones. Trucker John showed me how to lay the stones and build out his patio. Every stone would get laid down in a special way so they would all fit together. Trucker John was like an artist when he taught me how to lay the stones down. He would show me how they should fit together properly, then he would wipe away some sand and move them around ever so slightly. It was like he was getting lost in his work. Very much how I felt when I would go to the gym. It was always this place where I could lose myself and find myself at the same time.

This took me another hour and by now, I was completely drenched in sweat, covered in dirt and sand. When I finished laying all the bricks, there was still more work to be done but there was no more stone left.

I stood there staring at all the work I had done. I wasn't even sure why I stopped to stare at everything. I was exhausted and actually happy that there were no more stones left. Marie had been out for the entire time with her country music and fancy drinks. She had a few drinks while I was out there. It seemed like every hour she went in and came back out with another fancy drink. I must have been staring off into space until Trucker John came outside and stood next to me as I was staring at the patio.

He looked around for a few seconds and started grinning and nodding his head. He said to me, "Good work, Kid. Take a look at all the work you've done in just 3 hours. It's not finished yet but you can take it all in and see the progress. I doubt any kid your age is doing this kind of work let alone getting out of bed yet!"

I also grinned and nodded my head. I didn't say a word but I was most happy that I made Trucker John proud of me. Trucker John looked at me and I think he could read my mind. He saw I was proud of myself. Marie yelled out from the deck as she raised her fancy glass in the air, "Good work, Kid!"

Trucker John handed me money and I didn't count it. I just said "thank you" and put it in my pocket which was sweaty and soaking wet. John said to me, "You thirsty, Kid?" I replied, "No, I'm fine." Deep down, I was thirsty. Very THIRSTY! But I had just done all this work and there was this part of me that knew NOT to announce that I was thirsty or that I needed to reward myself with lemonade or anything else. I saw from Trucker John that the real reward was in doing the work.

After I declined a drink, Trucker John said to me, "Good. When I was a Ranger, we would go through training for hours without water and sometimes two days without food or sleep. Being a Ranger taught me how much the body can handle if the mind is willing. I wanted you to learn a little bit of that today. That's why I didn't get you a drink. Marie was gonna get you a drink but I stopped her." Trucker John laughed to himself when he said that and I laughed too.

"Listen, Kid. You can't let shit hold you back. Not a house, not a job, not a pretty girl, nothing. This world is tough and if you're not tough, well, you're gonna get your ass kicked, Kid. Plain and simple, that's how life works. Let me tell ya... I used to work for a company before I started trucking. I showed up early, stayed late. I went above and beyond and outworked everyone, even on my worst day. And then one day, when the recession hit, they didn't care. They let me go. I outworked everyone in that place. They had meetings and people I took care of did not take care of me. They didn't have the balls to stand up for a guy who had their back. I learned my lesson."

We both just stood there quietly for a few seconds but it seemed like an hour went by. I felt horrible for Trucker John. It was strange but I actually felt him hurting. It's like I was sharing his pain that moment. I could feel this weird feeling in my stomach and heart. I remember that day like it was yesterday, how my heart was actually hurting.

After a minute of silence, Trucker John took a deep breath and said to me, "And sometimes, Kid, a man needs to be alone. A man needs to go out into the woods and find out more about himself. Ya gotta get away from the noise. Get away from people. Get away from things that distract you and find out more about who you are. When it's time for you to do this one day, Kid, you'll know. You probably don't understand me now, Kid. But, one day you will. One day this conversation will all make sense to you. Alright Kid, get out of here and I'll see you when I see you."

I said "Thank you, John." We shook hands and Trucker John grinned and nodded his head, looking me square in the eyes as if he was proud of what he saw in me. From there, I got on my bike and hit the road. My ride home felt empty in a way. I had this strange empty feeling in my stomach that I had never felt before. I was sad, in a way. But I also was starting to understand, at this very moment, that life IS tough. There will be good times and bad times. There will be light and there will be darkness.

When I got home 15 minutes later, I emptied my pocket and saw Trucker John had paid me $30 bucks this time. I put the money in my wallet, took a shower and went downstairs as my Mom had made a plate of pancakes for me. I crushed those pancakes and drank 3 glasses of milk. I was starving after working in Trucker John's yard.

After I ate and filled up, I took my dog, Oz, for a walk. My dog seemed happier than ever to see me. My legs, back and forearms had this heavy feeling to them. Normally I ran with my Oz, this time, we just walked. We walked for a solid 45 minutes and when we got home, Oz drank his water and then sat down next to me as I put my back up against a tree.

This was my dog's way of saying thank you for the walk. He pushed his body against mine and laid his head on my lap. I put my hand on him and closed my eyes for a few seconds. A few seconds turned into a 90 minute nap for the both of us.

I woke up and had this realization how it was so great to do the simple things; lifting weights, manual labor, eating pancakes and spending time with your dog.

That week at the gym I didn't see Trucker John. Not on Monday, not on Tuesday, not on Wednesday. Honestly, by Wednesday, I was worried. One of Trucker John's training partners walked up to me on Thursday. He said "Hey, Kid. John's gonna be away for a while and he wanted me to give you this, alright?"

He handed me an envelope. I thanked him and put the envelope in my gym bag. His friend looked sad. He didn't have the usual pep he had like when they trained with Trucker John.

Later that night when I got home, I went straight to my room and closed the door. I opened up my gym bag and opened up the envelope from Trucker John. There was cash in the envelope as well. Ten $100 bills. They were crisp and clean. Brand new. The money didn't hit me at first as I was concerned only with what Trucker John wrote in the letter.

The letter said, "Hey, Kid. I'll be gone for a while so I wanted to let you know. I put some money in here for you and I want you to take care of the yard for me while I'm away. Marie knows you'll be showing up. Get there once a week and keep the place looking good. Everything is in the garage. I've got your address so I'll be in touch, Kid. Until then, I'll see ya when I see ya."

I folded the letter and placed it back in the envelope. I had a drawer on my desk where I kept my money and I put this letter in there as well. I was sad and felt that strange pit in my stomach and heart. Trucker John had never been to my house but he knew where I lived. He was a smart guy. His presence had energy that you could feel a mile away.

Every weekend, usually on Sunday, I would mow the lawn and trim the edges at Trucker John's house. In the Fall, I raked the leaves. In the Winter, if it snowed, I was there shoveling. Marie would always be looking out the window when it was cold. She smiled and waved and would check back every 10 minutes.

In the Summer time it was the same. She'd be out on that deck sun bathing with her fancy, tall drinks. She had that beautiful smile whenever she said, "Hey, Kid!" Her eyes were blue, like the ocean. After 2 years of taking care of Trucker John's yard, I remember seeing a House for Sale sign on the front lawn.

I didn't see Marie in the window or the backyard like usual. Instead, a lady walked out the front door to greet me. I can't even recall her name. I think I was in too much shock that Marie was not around anymore. It was the end of something, I just wasn't sure what.

The realtor greeted me like John and Marie always did. She called me "Kid." She told me she had heard about me and loved how beautiful the yard looked. She told me this would be my last time mowing the lawn as the new homeowners will be doing that themselves.

I asked her if Marie was ok and she replied, "Oh yea, Kid. She's never been better. She's on the road to Montana to be with John." I smiled. I told her I'll make the yard look great for her. She replied, "I know you will, Kid. I heard all about you."

I mowed that lawn with precision like never before. I edged the grass, swept the sidewalk, the driveway and the patio. Mid way into mowing the lawn I got that feeling again. That feeling in my stomach and heart. I tried not to cry but I cried. I cried while mowing the lawn and my tears mixed with the sweat streaming down my face.

I knew this was my last time taking care of John and Marie's lawn. When I finished mowing the lawn I rode my bike to the nursery that was close by, maybe a mile away. I had money with me and asked the owner to help me. Before I could introduce myself to the owner said to me, "Hey Kid, I know who you are. You take care of John and Marie's place. You do great work. Very impressive. How can I help you?"

I replied, "Well, the house is for sale and I'd like to buy some flowers for the front and backyard. I have $100. I want to buy as much as I can for $100." The owner said, "You sure, Kid? That's a lot of money." Truth is, I didn't care about the money. I said, "I also need someone to deliver them to the house for me. I'll take care of everything from there."

We walked around and picked out a bunch of different flowers. I remember I didn't even know what any of them were. But, I did see some giant sunflowers. They seemed perfect for the backyard near the deck that Marie always sunbathed on.

I gave the owner my $100 bill. It was still crisp and clean, just like it was two years ago when I got it. I rode my bike back to the house and a few minutes later the flowers were dropped off for me. I mulched the front garden and planted the flowers. I mulched the side of the house and planted more flowers.

And then backyard. This backyard was special and it hit me right then for some reason. I planted the giant sunflowers and gave the back deck and stone patio a final sweeping.

When I finished, I just took a step back and took it all in. The house looked beautiful. It was quiet out and I could hear the familiar sounds of Marie and John calling me "Kid" all the time. I remembered Marie's blue eyes and her smile. I remember John's chiseled face. He had that tough look all the time but deep down you knew he cared about you.

A few minutes later I heard people outside. I heard a lady say "Oh my God, I love this backyard. It's beautiful here." It was a couple walking around the house with the realtor. The realtor saw me standing in the back as the couple stood next to her and admired how beautiful the backyard looked. She winked at me and I could read her mind as if she was saying to me, "Good work, Kid. You're gonna be alright."

I waited for the couple to go inside and I quietly walked around the house. Before I walked through the fence to exit the backyard for the final time, I turned around and took it all in for a few seconds. I looked at the beautiful backyard. The patio. The flowers. The mulch that went all around the perimeter. I took a lot of pride in what that backyard became. I think John knew exactly what he was doing. He was teaching me to take pride. Teaching me that anything worthy is going to take time. It's not gonna take weeks, months or even years.

I opened the gate and quietly closed it. It was as if I was leaving a dojo of sorts and would not be returning. I felt that pit in my stomach when I closed the gate and heard the "click" of the latch.

I walked across the driveway and remembered John and I sweeping and hosing off the sand from the driveway. That lesson was how good enough is the death of greatness. That staying for a few more minutes to put the finishing touches on something is the difference between good and great. As I walked down the driveway I heard the echoes of John and Marie saying, "Great work, Kid."

I hopped on my bike and rode home. Normally I would really push myself on my bike, pedaling aggressively and jumping curbs, like I was attacking the streets. Not this time. This time, I sat down and pedaled slowly. I was happy and sad at the same time. Sad that I would not be cutting the grass again because I took so much pride in it. But most of all, happy that Marie was going to be with John. It was as if they could not live without one another. That was perfect. That made me happy. Marie let John do his thing for 2 years, whatever that thing was. And after 2 years apart, they were heading on their next adventure together.

Chapter 2:

RUDY

Rudy was a quiet man. He trained in the outdoors, enjoying the peace of mind from being in nature. He didn't pay much mind to the news or what "other people" thought of him. Instead, he loved what he loved and left it at that. He never pushed his opinions on anyone and only shared his thoughts when people asked.

To each his own, is how he always thought.

Rudy reminded me of the famous poem by Tecumseh.

"So live your life that the fear of death can never enter your heart. Trouble no one about their religion; respect others in their view, and demand that they respect yours. Love your life, perfect your life, beautify all things in your life. Seek to make your life long and its purpose in the service of your people. Prepare a noble death song for the day when you go over the great divide.

Always give a word or a sign of salute when meeting or passing a friend, even a stranger, when in a lonely place. Show respect to all people and grovel to none.

When you arise in the morning give thanks for the food and for the joy of living. If you see no reason for giving thanks, the fault lies only in yourself. Abuse no one and no thing, for abuse turns the wise ones to fools and robs the spirit of its vision.

When it comes your time to die, be not like those whose hearts are filled with the fear of death, so that when their time comes they weep and pray for a little more time to live their lives over again in a different way. Sing your death song and die like a hero going home."

— Chief Tecumseh

I met Rudy at The Avenel Health & Racquet club. My buddy was a member there and he always had guest passes. I'm not sure if my buddy stole these guest passes because he had well over 100 of them. I would go once a week with my friend, often 2 or 3 times a week.

My friend was on the smaller side and his Dad was always nagging him to train to get bigger and stronger so his Dad signed him up for the racquet club. This place was HUGE. There were indoor tennis and racquet courts, a swimming pool, a fitness area that was divided into different spaces with machines, free weights, an aerobics room and then an indoor track that surrounded the entire fitness area.

There was a wide variety of people training at this place, from big money makers who worked in NYC to Pro Wrestlers from the '80s and everyone in between.

Rudy saw my buddy and I trying to learn to squat on a special bar we had never seen before. The bar had pads that went over our shoulders and when we squatted, we would place our hands on what looked like handlebars.

Rudy was training with a few guys, two of them we recognized from TV. They were pro wrestlers and even though I wasn't into the pro wrestling thing, we all knew who they were. These guys stood out because of how large they were.

Their shirts were stretched by their enormous arms and chest. I never saw such huge traps on a man like these guys. Their traps raised up through their shirts like softballs. Their necks were wider than their heads. They looked scary but they were always laughing, smiling and joking around.

Rudy walked up to my buddy and said, "Boys, that right there is called the safety squat bar. The man who invented it is from Trenton, NJ. His name is Jesse Hoagland. Today, some people call it The Hatfield bar because the powerlifter who popularized this bar is Dr. Fred Hatfield, aka Dr. Squat."

My buddy and I were in awe of Rudy and his friends so we just smiled and said nothing. Rudy must have thought we were two knuckleheads, and rightfully so.

As we stared and smiled speechless, Rudy said, "Let me show you guys how to use this bar and then you can get going."

Rudy demonstrated how to get under the safety bar, how to walk the bar out in a methodical manner, how to take a deep breath before squatting and how to "come out of the hole."

After he demonstrated the squat, he said to my friend and I, "Alright, boys. Let's see each of you get a set of 5 to warm up. We'll watch you." Rudy's pro wrestling buddies walked up.We were now surrounded by the three biggest guys in the entire racquet club.

I was nervous and I am sure my buddy Steve was as well. We had no choice here but to shut up and lift. Rudy talked both of us through each portion of the squat.

"Boys, first of all, get your head out of your ass. When you squat, it's not the time to be thinking about anything else. Not your girlfriend, not your homework, nothing. OK, grab that fuckin' bar and hold the handles TIGHT. Good, now get under the bar and squeeze your back. Your back is a shelf for the bar. Get tight! Good, now get directly under the bar and squat it up. Excellent! Now, take two steps back. Good.

"Here we go. Take a deep breath. Squat down slowly and EXPLODE. Good, now do four more. Down slow, EXPLODE! Excellent, again!"

"OK, boys, if 5 reps is easy, which it was, add more weight." Rudy's wrestling buddies took another step closer as my buddy and I looked at each other and said, 'Let's add a 10."

One of the wrestlers shouted and said, "Fuck those 10s. Put a plate on, boys!" My buddy and I looked at each other, smiled and both said, "OK!"

I remember climbing up to 185 that day. A 45 and a 25 lb plate on each side. Normally I took small jumps of 5 or 10 lb plates and worked up to 165. The energy was electric for me! I had seen Pumping **IRON** the documentary and I would get psyched up watching the Arnold vs Lou scene with everyone shouting and pushing their training partners. I was finally experiencing what this was REALLY like.

I was 14 at the time and never really trained with this intensity. The wrestlers introduced themselves to my buddy and I. They were Jimmy and Billy. They shook our hands and said, "Solid work, boys. That's what it takes and it's good to see some young guys in here working."

My buddy Steve and I both said "Thank you." Rudy and the wrestlers nodded and smiled at us and told us they would see us soon. Truth is, Steve was my buddy but he was not as passionate about training as I was although he was much more gifted than I was. He was a natural athlete and a solid 20 or 25 lbs bigger than me.

He was basically training because his Dad was forcing him to train. His Dad would lecture the entire way to and from the racquet club. Then, Steve would get home and his Dad would have him running around the block with ankle weights. Then go inside and stretch on this Chuck Norris stretching machine that puts you in a split for your legs.

My Dad never did that stuff. He was busy working and I honestly don't think my Dad knew what I should do. My Dad grew up in Romania and Israel. When in Romania, he told me every three months he and his classmates would stand in their boxers and sport coaches would come to weigh them and measure their height.

Every 3 or 6 months, the Coach would tell someone the two sports the kid was suited for. My Dad was put into Boxing and Swimming. Other kids went to Wrestling and Gymnastics. Taller kids went to Water Polo and Basketball.

The genetically gifted kids would eat in a different cafeteria and it was called 'Super Elementation Cafeteria'. My dad said they basically had MORE food available and could go online unlimited times to get food.

My dad told me that half the day was school and the other half was training for sport or Physical Education. Outside the school was a mountain and a ski lift. The athletes would be spread out on various areas of the mountain. Outside, the wrestlers dragged their mat on the grass when the weather was warm. Weightlifters were constantly maxing out. My Dad would often perform hill sprints with his team while a Coach rode up and down the mountain on the ski lift.

When my Dad was 12, he broke his nose boxing. The Coach shoved tissue in the nose and wrapped tape around his head and he had to continue training. When my Dad moved to Israel to escape communism in Romania, his family moved to a Kibbutz. My Dad worked all day to earn his meals.

I guess my Dad thought it was the same in America. Figure it out and fight for what you want. You get what you earn, ultimately, not what you want. I think my Dad was just happy because he saw me doing something with consistency. Training every day, eating healthy and reading a LOT of bodybuilding books and magazines.

Steve's Dad forced it on him. Steve liked training, but he did NOT LOVE the TRAINING. He did NOT love the work. We still had a great time when we trained. I realized that for Steve, he always would have been up for doing something else. Not me. I LOVED training and whether I was training or in a gym, I was at my happiest. I felt the best.

I knew training at the racquet club would eventually come to an end with Steve. But, for a few months, this training continued. Most of the time, we ran into Rudy, Jimmy and Billy.

Rudy was always helping us out. Jimmy and Billy just followed Rudy. I used to get fired up knowing Rudy would always share a story or a training tip with Steven and me. On one particular day, we were planning on doing chest and back.

I was very weak on the bench. Steve was much stronger than I was at benching but I was starting to surpass him on exercises like squats and pull ups. I just wanted to get bigger and stronger so freakin' badly, I think I was WILLING myself to grow.

On the day that we were benching, Rudy saw Steve and me loading up the bar to get warmed up. He nodded his head from afar as he saw us getting started and I waved. After my first set, Rudy walked over and said, 'What's up, boys? What do we got today?" Steve replied, "Chest and Back!"

Rudy replied, "Oh yes, Monday, international chest day... hahaha." I had no clue what Rudy meant when he said that or why he was laughing. Rudy said, "OK, boys, let's see what your technique looks like. Add some weight and go ahead."

I benched 95 lb and banged out 10 reps. Steven took off the quarters and we added a plate. Steve banged out 4 reps, then I spotted him for a 5th rep, and then he tried for a 6th rep but I had to pull the bar off his chest. Mid way through the rep while he was grinding out the rep, he just gave up and let the bar drop to his chest.

While Rudy was watching, Jimmy and Billy walked over and nodded to us as they watched. I think they knew Rudy was about to rip into us. After Steve's set he started giving us his advices.

"Steve. Holy shit, man. First of all, don't ever let a bar collapse on you. I don't care if you're squatting or benching. That's unacceptable. If you're going for the rep, MAKE THE REP. Don't give up in the middle of a rep. You need to change that shitty attitude, son. We call it "Make the Rep or Die!" Do you understand me?"

Rudy actually seemed pissed and I felt bad for Steve but at the same time, that mindset Rudy just explained was awesome. "Make the Rep or Die." Then Rudy looked at me and said, "Zach. Don't ever spot someone benching with a curl grip or with fingers. Your hands should be double overhand or over / under mixed grip like a deadlift. Now, no one is gonna get hurt with that chicken shit weight, but one day when you're benching 275, 315 or more, the spotter is NOT going to curl the weight off your chest. And that two finger spot. Forget it. Never do that shit. It's dangerous as you can tell. Steve gave up and then you had to figure out how to pull the weight off his chest."

"OK, for this next set, Steve, don't do any forced reps. Just do three reps. I want you to stop right before you think you're gonna need a spotter. Learn to do the work on your own. Zach, you're gonna do 135. No more going back to the quarters and dimes from here."

I was nervous because I'd benched 135 for a single a few times, but never more. So I knew not to argue. I replied, "Sounds good!" Rudy and his buddies stepped away for a few minutes and walked over to the squat rack. They each did their set of Hatfield Squats. Steve and I watched and I remember being in awe of how strong those guys were. And those plates. WOW. The plates on the bar were rumbling. There were five plates on each side of the bar.

These guys were intense. While one guy squatted, another guy spotted and then the third guy was shouting technique cues. It was a fine oiled machine. They each did 8 reps. After all three went, they added another plate to each side.

Rudy was especially fired up as he squatted last. When he finished his set and racked it, he let out a loud, "Wooooo! Too easy!" The guys laughed and walked back over.

Rudy told me to bench first. "Alright, Zach. Lay down and let me walk you through this. Line up so your eyes are under the bar. Grab the knurling an inch, maybe slightly wider than an inch from the smooth. You guys were gripping the bar too wide and lowering the bar too high. You're gonna lower the bar below your nipple line, basically to the sternum. Go down slowly, then explode up. Zach, get your shit together here and do three reps. You understand me!?"

I said, "Yes!" What the heck else was I gonna say? I was scared to let down Rudy and fired up to start benching 135. It was a big accomplishment to finally bench with a plate on each side.

I laid back on the bench and lined up with my eyes under the bar. Then I checked each hand to make sure both were equally grabbing the knurling like he said. While doing this, Rudy said, "Do NOT rush the set up. Now, squeeze your shoulder blades so they are tight to the bench, like eagle claws. Press your feet into the floor so you feel tight. Good. I'll give you a lift off. Count it off and I'll spot you." Rudy basically was telling Steve to get out of the way and wake up.

I counted loud, "3. 2. 1!" Rudy gave me a lift off and it was different from what Steve would do. Steve would rip the bar and I'd sometimes feel like I was losing my position on the bench. Rudy gave this perfect lift off. I felt very strong with the way he showed me how to set up and perform the bench.

I took the bar down slowly to my sternum and then pressed up the first rep. The first rep was easy! I felt like it was literally launching off my chest. Rudy said, "Good! Now two more!" I did the second rep, BOOM! Then a third rep, BOOM! The third rep was tough, But I definitely had another one in me.

Rudy said to me, "Dude, that was perfect! You see how your entire body needs to work when benching? It's a FULL body exercise. Not just a chest exercise like you guys think. I want you to do two more sets of three reps. So basically 3 x 3 with that same weight. And you left one in the tank. This keeps technique in check and helps you get stronger. Steve, don't do all that forced rep shit. You don't get strong that way. You just get good at failing. You hear me?"

Steve nodded his head and I can tell Steve was disappointed in himself and kind of embarrassed. Steve did a set of four, then two sets of three. I got my three sets of three and felt strong.

My shoulder also didn't hurt like it often did when benching and lowering the bar so high on our chest. While we were benching, Rudy and his buddies hit their last set of squats.

When they walked to the squat rack they were loud. Rudy told Jimmy and Billy, "Alright, let's fucking GO!" It was intense watching them train. It's as if they transformed into someone else. Rudy and his buddies were so welcoming when they chatted with us. But when they trained, they got fired up. I watched all of them squat with 6 plates on each side. The plates were rumbling and man, I LOVED that sound. All three of the guys did 6 reps.

Rudy's (cabin) home was off the beaten path and he liked it that way. I remember the first time I drove there it was already dark and kind of spooky to be honest. Driving through the woods for what seemed to be 10 minutes to get to Rudy's cabin reminded me of where they filmed the movie Friday the 13th.

But then, during the day when the sun was shining, WOW, the place was absolutely stunning. It looked like a painting, almost as if it was too perfect to actually be real.

Rudy's cabin was simple. It was a cabin with a fireplace. The sink was set in stone and the table was built from granite and wood. I had never seen anything like it. It was a masterpiece and one of a kind, all of which Rudy built himself.

There was no TV or internet in Rudy's cabin. It was the ultimate minimalist living space. Rudy had an old couch, a recliner and two bookshelves. **IRON**ically, that old couch was more comfortable than any other couch I'd ever sat on. Your body would melt into that couch and you felt like you were floating when you sat on it.

Rudy had a beautiful dog that followed him everywhere he went. The loyalty of Rudy's dog reminded me of my first Doberman, Oz. Oz would sleep against my door until I woke up in the morning. If my door was open, he would sleep under my bed. He protected me at all times. Rudy's dog was named Koda.

In one corner of the cabin, Rudy had his fishing poles scattered along with a pair of snowshoes and tackle boxes. Rudy also had a few guns for hunting that hung on the cabin wall.

Outside of his cabin, Rudy had a squat rack he built from wood.

The barbell stayed loaded on the squat rack with one or two plates on each side at all times. The plates were all deep dish York plates. When Rudy trained, he warmed up with basic calisthenics and some odd dumbbells that were scattered around the perimeter of his cabin.

Sometimes Rudy would grab some small stones and warm up with arm circles, shoulder raises and even throwing the small stones. The small stones were about the size of a shot put.

Rudy had welded a few clubs. They looked like what you see Indian wrestlers training with. Rudy would swing them around his body with one and two arm motions.

The dumbbells were also welded and had different handles than normal dumbbells. They were all thick handles. I recall one of the dumbbells my fingers could not wrap around fully, it must have been three inches thick.

When Rudy trained, he crushed the volume. With nowhere to go and no one to answer to, I guess you can say time was on his side. He shared his training with me and it inspired me to follow suit in my garage when all I had was a squat rack, a flat utility bench, a few Kettlebells and bands.

I didn't even have dumbbells in my garage so I used the Kettlebells for my rep work when pressing and rowing.

When I say my friend had nowhere to go and no one to see, I mean it. He was an absolute loner except for his dog and an occasional visit from a friend every other month to so.

He saved his money from his work where he was a builder of custom homes. People loved his work because he rarely used heavy machines like the other builders. He would break the concrete with a sledge hammer while others used a jack hammer.

He was also a local guide for hunters and fishermen.

People only found out about him through word of mouth. No website or email. Instead, messages were left for him at the post office or the general store.

His fishing and hunting trips never disappointed anyone.

His free time was for reading, training and of course solo trips for fishing and hunting.

He told me that sometimes he would go out in the woods with nothing but a pack of matches to see how long he could survive with nothing but the clothing on his back.

I think those "trips" were a sort of a Warrior's journey for him.

I also think the hard training served as his IRON therapy.

It certainly always does for me and I believe that's why we connected. We BOTH trained for the mental aspect, NOT just the muscle building benefits.

He didn't care if the weather was cold. He still trained outside, regardless of the weather. Yes, even in the snow.

He told me that he didn't just lift heavy or just lift for high reps.

He trained according to the journey he wanted to go on.

He wanted to learn about himself.

He told me about how he would adjust the tempo of the reps along with adding pause reps.

He felt the slow tempo and the pauses REALLY built up his strength and density.

Fighting those eccentrics made him tough, he told me.

It was brutal and when he went through these phases of training he increased his quality calories.

He would eat the game that he hunted and his carbs were basic: fresh fruits, sweet potatoes, carrots, and other veggies.

If it was Winter he would keep a large pot on the stove with beef and vegetable stew.

When he finished his volume training he transitioned to a minimalist plan, training only 2 x week.

My friend was strong yet silent.

He loved life. He was also a giver.

He would go to town and give some of his veggies from his garden to random people.

He would bring extra meat he couldn't keep in his large freezer and give it to the butcher.

He asked the butcher to gift it to people after they bought something from his store.

He never asked for anything in return.

He didn't keep score.

He was just a good human.

How rare.

Rudy
Part II

took a trip a few days ago to meet an old friend, Rudy.

Rudy had been "Quarantining" looooong before it was the "New Normal".

He went into the military after high school and worked his way into Special Forces.
Once he retired from the Military he laid low.

His hobbies?

- Finding old, classic pick up trucks and restoring them.
- Lifting Weights.
- Cooking.
- Hunting.
- Fishing.
- Reading.
- Cooking.

Rudy purchased a small ranch home on a large lot of land. There is a small pond on his land and he catches some BIG Bass.

Some of them he lost in combat, others he lost touch with after he retired..

He felt like his best friends were the things he had around him, not necessarily people.

The old cars he got to work on.

The sound of nature he could listen to day and night.

The clear night sky and the stars above every night.

And the **IRON**. We spoke about Henry Rollins' poem *"The **IRON** Never Lies"* and he told me it's so true.

He told me, *"Veterans NEED the **IRON***. The **IRON** is great therapy. Working on my trucks, hunting and fishing. Working with our hands.We NEED that"

I asked him if I could come up next time and learn a bit about working on cars and he had the biggest smile..

He responded, "Oh hells yea, brother. That would be great."

We walked another 10 minutes or so and didn't say a word to one another.

We didn't have to.

We enjoyed the "things" around us.

And I was VERY grateful.

Those moments and times with friends are special.

I hope you find them yourself, too.

RUDY: LIFE & LIFTING LESSONS

After our training session together, Rudy and I sat on his front porch for a few minutes.....

Rudy brought out a tall glass of raw milk and he served it to me in a mason jar.

I thanked him and told him how I NEEDED that tough training session.

He smirked at me and raised his glass.

We both sat there, our bodies felt worked.

As I sat there, I got this feeling that Rudy KNEW I needed to be up there.

Rudy would always call me randomly, as if he knew it was time for me to get away and travel to see him.

It's as if he could stare into my soul and hear the call of the wild for me, so to speak.

We both sat on the edge of his porch and enjoyed this feeling we got after training, yet we didn't have to say a word about it.

It's a feeling that ONLY the hardest of workers can understand. We chase that feeling.

It goes deeper than a big chest or big arms, that's for damn sure.

I stared off into the woods for a few minutes yet it seemed like hours and I just took it all in.

The sights, the sounds and even the smell.

My senses always came alive on Rudy's property.

I guzzled down that glass of raw milk and it tasted a bit different than normal.

Rudy said to me, *I put some raw honey in there to give it a little sweetness. It's great after a hard training session. Better than those protein shakes we used to drink in the late 80s and early 90s! ha ha*

I thought to myself, *Damn right, I have never tasted something so good in ages.*

Rudy put his mason jar down and started walking.

He didn't say anything to me so I just started following him.

We began to take a walk around his property.

The sun was starting to cool off but I was still sweating buckets.

The air was clean, though. I could feel the cool air starting to help my body calm itself down.
It was a reminder of how beautiful it was in nature.

Not that I don't love living by the beach.

I most certainly do.

But there was something pure and clean about being so close to the mountains.

Rudy and I began to share our random thoughts in a strange world. I said to Rudy, *"Man, the world is a crazy place and I don't fit into it anymore."*

He laughed so loud and I began laughing with him.

His laugh sounded like it came straight from the '80s movie Predator, when Billy would laugh and the Predator could hear him.

He said, *"Brother, I figured that out in the late '90s. I saw it coming as soon as that damn internet thing got popular."*

Rudy asked me how my business was going.

He said to me, "I bet your most popular courses are the ones that are short, easy and convenient."

He said this with a nice touch of sarcasm.

I replied to him, *"What's very interesting is that after almost 20 years of offering online coaching through my training courses, and I do mean VERY interesting, especially the past 5-7 years or so, has been how people are starting to REALLY look for the short cuts.*

The easy way.

What is the fastest way?"

Rudy nodded his head with a smirk and his smirk quickly changed to a look of disappointment.

Rudy then took a deep breath and I knew a rant was in the works here.

He said, *"I bet your Volume Course and The big manual* (Rudy was referring to The Underground Strength System) you have are the LEAST popular." He continued, *"People don't want to fight for results.*

They want it handed to them. You need to be willing to make less money while staying true to yourself.

I knew you were a worker when I met you the first time. You were a skinny little kid but you would train for 2 hours.

I could see your work ethic a mile away."

I replied to Rudy, *"You're right... You are always right."*

Rudy said to me, *"Eh, not always, but most of the time!"*

Then he belted out that loud laugh of his and I swear to you his laugh scared all the animals within a 3 mile radius.

I then shared with Rudy a story I had heard while listening to a podcast, where I heard the phrase, *"Your body is your business card."*

What these two Coaches said in this podcast was that this is specific to those who are private business owners / coaches.

Why?

Well, one of the guys on the podcast had Coached in The NFL, he has trained celebs, pro athletes and he himself was a world class athlete 20 years ago.

He went on to say,*"In the pros or the college sector, it's all about delivering results. But if you're private and on the internet promoting yourself, people only judge you by what you look like."*

He added, *"So they see a 22 year old who took anabolics and he's big and ripped yet telling people how to train to achieve his results and then people buy into that Bull S--t."*

Rudy said, *"Listen, pal, people in today's world , people only judge you by looks, and THAT is their reality.*

Their perception is their reality.

They don't care what kind of person you are.

They want more of that fake popularity BS that so many people chase on a computer.

The truth is they need more of THIS. What you and I are doing right here.

They don't want hard work.

They don't want tough workouts like your Volume Training Course.

They want some vitamins and some dumbbells and bodyweight bull s--t.

You're ripped? I Trust You.

Photos with celebrities? I Trust You."

Rudy went on to say, *"Zach, that's what I like about you.*

You've stayed true to who you are.

Yes, I've seen you lose your way sometimes but you always come back to living your truth.

You've always been a worker.

You've always wanted to earn everything.

You never wanted a free handout.

You'll never be the most popular with that kind of honest work ethic but you will ALWAYS be able to walk with pride knowing you never faked it.

Just keep living your truth, brother."

From there, we kept walking until the sun began to set.

When we got back to Rudy's cabin he had a large pot of beef and potatoes that had been simmering on the stove top.

We were about to eat and shut it down for the night.

The long drive up to Rudy's cabin started to kick in and as we sat down to eat, I told Rudy how grateful I am that we have been friends for 30 years now.

He replied, *"Zach, I am also grateful.... I always will be."*

CHAPTER 3:

UNCLE TONY'S HIGHWAY GYM

Uncle Tony's Highway Gym was a place I came across while driving home from a family gathering.

I was just 16, maybe 15 at the time...We were driving home from The Bronx.

I saw the gym from the car and asked my Dad to pull over and he did. My Dad knew I was addicted to training. He would take me on my visit to gyms and I would ask the front desk person questions about the business.

I was a young teen and knew I wanted to own a gym. NEVER did I think I'd be doing what I do today because let's face it, what I do today was NOT happening anywhere in the world in 1991.

My Dad waited in the car as I walked into Uncle Tony's Gym. This was a small space in a strip plaza and the equipment was as basic as you get..

I saw more squat racks than the norm. Half of this gym had squat racks and power cages.

The guys training there were Big and Strong.

Def Leppard was blasting on the stereo and there were speakers in all four corners of the gym.

No one was at the front desk so I waited two minutes and then started walking around. Out of the 18 guys in the gym, not one of them gave me a head nod.

I could tell this place was not the norm. It would be a place where I'd have to EARN respect.

The guys were benching. Some were dumbbell benching. Another guy was doing triceps pushdowns with the entire weight stack plus a 45 lb plate pinned to the stack for extra.

He was a HOUSE. He was wearing a white tank top and his arms were MASSIVE. He had a long beard and wore a beat up baseball cap.

A few guys were deadlifting and one guy was inside of a power cage. He was squatting from the pins. Starting from the bottom.

This guy was MASSIVE.

His upper body was stretching through his thermal shirt with sleeves cut off. His legs were stretching sweatpants.

He finished his set and the weights clanged together LOUDLY on his last rep. He was doing pin squats with 585 (6 plates per side).

He was sweating bullets and saw me, walked up and introduced himself as "Uncle Tony" "I own this place.", he said to me.

At first I thought he meant, he OWNED this place because he was THE strongest guy. Then I got my $0.02 cents together and realized he literally AND figuratively owned the gym.

He told me to look around and let him know if I had any questions. I walked around and saw this place as a REAL gym. I had been in some REAL gyms but man, this place was a new level.

I was scared but I knew I needed this. I needed a place to get out of my comfort zone. I needed that loud music.

I needed a place that would take me to new levels in wrestling and strength. This place would be my next move.

I got to my car and told my Dad about the gym. I told him about Uncle Tony and he must have been wondering who the f--k "Uncle Tony" is.

Being 15 or 16 at the time, I was clueless but my Dad probably thought Uncle Tony was part of the NJ mob and this gym was a cover up for moving money.

From what I saw, the only thing moving was BIG weights.

I always saved my money for two things:

1) Gym Membership

2) Protein Shakes

I asked my Dad if I could join the gym and he mentioned it was not as close as the other gym I was going to.

In fact, the other gym was 5 minutes away, and this gym would be 20 minutes away.

But I told him that I NEEDED to be at this gym. THIS would be THE place that helps me become GREAT at wrestling. Deep down, I just wanted to get HUGE, I did not know what the effects would be on my wrestling.

The next day was Monday and my Mom drove me to the new gym after her work and my Dad picked me up on the way home from his work. I had a solid two hours to train but I also brought my bookbag to do homework and study.

I got to the gym around 4 PM and the music was blasting. Some bands I had heard of like Pantera, Metallica, Megadeth, BioHazard. Other bands were more of a Vietnam era playlist like Creedence Clearwater Revival (CCR), Chuck Berry, The Doors and Lynyrd Skynyrd.

It wasn't too busy at 4 PM since most folks usually worked until 5 PM. I saw Uncle Tony and he shook my hand really hard. I handed him 45 bucks and that I would like to sign up for the month.

He remembered my name..."*Zach, good to see you. Most kids your age never come back after stopping in. It's good to see you. Let's get your membership card filled out.*"

The membership card was AWESOME.

It said Uncle Tony's Gym and there was a pic of a BIG guy Deadlifting with a LONG beard. THAT pic was of Uncle Tony.

I put the card in my small gym bag and went on one of the stationary bikes to warm up for five minutes. I was planning on Squatting afterward. After all, it was Monday and also, legs were my strongest body part.

If I was gonna earn ANY respect here, today would be my chance since my bench sucked.

After warming up on the bike, I went through my weight warm up. Two sets of 20 reps of leg extensions, leg curls and leg press. This always got me a great pump and I felt better when it was time to squat.

Every five minutes a new guy walked in to train. The crowd was picking up and now there were about 12 guys in the gym. Nobody was skinny. They were either big, powerlifting type guys or lean and muscular guys.

Not one person acknowledged me.

I KNEW I was gonna have to Squat my heaviest on this day! As I began to put a 45 lb plate on each side of the bar, Jimi Hendrix was blaring through Uncle Tony's Gym.

I saw a guy playing air guitar in between his sets of benching. That guy was short and stocky. He was benching 315. Alone. In between sets he would sit down and do some music with his arms. Air guitar, drums, you name it, he was in his own world.

I saw him hit 365 for 4 reps from the corner of my eye. Then when he got to 405 I was thinking, "Damn, I can't even squat that weight and he's benching it!?!?"

One of the guys went up to spot him on the 405 and not a word was said to one another. It was like they knew each other and knew exactly what was needed and expected.

As Jimi Hendrix blasted through the gym, this guy benched 405 for 1, then 2, then 3 reps. On his last rep he grunted out LOUD. The weight was racked and he stood up and shouted, "YEA!!!"

By now the energy in the gym was at a new level. Everyone was moving weight. Except me. I was working up on my squats. I was at 275.

On the stereo a song came on by John Denver. It was "Take Me Home, Country Roads". A bunch of guys shouted and **IRON**ically, they all screamed, "Shut this sh-t off!!"

Someone skipped that song on the CD player and it went to CCR's song, Fortunate Son.

Uncle Tony walked to the back and checked up on me. He saw me squatting and said, "Alright Zach, let's see it!"

I grinned and nodded and got under the bar. I squatted 275 for 11 reps. Normally I could do 7 or 8 reps but I wanted to impress Uncle Tony.

I racked the bar and all the old York plates clanged together. Uncle Tony started talking to me and you could hear heavy dumbbells slamming to the ground and weights clanging all through the gym.

He said, "Open your stance up two inches on each foot and get lower. Go to 315 for 3 reps. From there I'll tell you how heavy to go after that. Even if you can do more than 3 reps, stop at 3."

I took off the quarters and got three 45 plates on each side of the bar. I felt like I somewhat fit in now that I had 315 on the bar. Next to me were 2 guys doing bent over barbell rows with an underhand grip.

They had 315 on the bar too.

The plates were rumbling and they were screaming at each other to *"Get one more, get one more!"* The "Get one more" started around 6 or 7 reps in and they would end up doing 12 or 13 reps and then slamming the weights down after the last rep.

Nobody cared if weights were being slammed. It was as if this was expected and this was normal activity. Uncle Tony didn't bat an eye when these guys were rowing.

From there they left the bar on the floor and began doing shrugs. No straps and double overhand grip. I remember they were switching how wide their grip was on each set and the first rep of each set was always from the floor. Deadlift the bar up, then shrug.

They went 315, 405 and then 5 plates at 495. When they got to 495 I heard one guy scream, *'Hook grip that shit!"*

I didn't know what that meant back then. But now I use this grip exclusively as I've "gotten older" to avoid straining a bicep with an over under grip. The hook grip is used extensively by weightlifters. Your index and middle finger wraps around your thumb and literally "hooks" the bar. You can handle immense poundages this way.

Now, back to those squats as Uncle Tony watched me. I went to my bag to grab my leather weightlifting belt and Uncle Tony said loudly, *"NO!"* I looked up at him confused and he said, *"NO belt. Do it on your own. It's only 315. When you get to 405 we can use a belt. Maybe."*

I had never squatted "heavy" without a belt and so this was a monkey wrench for me. I knew not to talk back to Uncle Tony or any of the guys. THAT was how you learned.

You showed up, worked hard, kept your mouth shut and hoped someone would help you. It was a sign of respect if they helped you and it never happened on day one. It's as if they counted the days you showed up to see if you were just there as a hobby or were you in it for the long haul.

As I stood up, Uncle Tony said to me, *"Zach. The squat begins in your mind. It begins even before you touch the bar. So visualize yourself destroying this sh-t and LET'S F—ING GO, MOTHER F—-ER!!"*

Uncle Tony slapped me on the back and I tried not to act shocked but deep down I thought to myself, *"Holy S—t! WTF did he hit me for!?!?"*

I was actually pissed off. I wanted to turn around and blast double him (that's a wrestling move) but somehow in that moment I turned my anger to the bar.

I grabbed the bar tighter than ever. I had goosebumps. CCR's Green River was blasting and in my peripheral I saw that stocky guy playing air guitar in front of the incline bench.

From there, my focus went solely to my squat rack. It was strange, I heard the music, I heard plates rumbling, dumbbells slamming to the floor but it was as if I was controlling the volume.

I squeezed my traps and back TIGHT. I squatted the bar up and walked back perfectly. two steps. One step with each foot. I squatted down on the first rep and it FLEW up. It felt like 135. I hit a second rep, EASY. As I was taking in a deep breath for my 3rd rep, Uncle Tony shouted, *"We're gonna do 10!"*

I know he said we were gonna do three but I guess he changed his mind. There was no time to argue. I just went down and up. The third rep was easy. Easier than ever before. At the eighth rep it got tough, but Uncle Tony shouted, "This is YOU!" I did rep nine and then before that 10th rep, I took three deep breaths and grinned the 10th rep.

I racked the bar and the plates clanged. I turned around with a big grin and Uncle Tony said, *"That's how it's done, Zach! That's what we like to see around here."*

I smiled and Uncle Tony walked away. I went to take off my weightlifting belt and realized it was NEVER on. I forgot it was still in the bag.

The guys shrugging next to me said, *"Nice set, Zach."* I never introduced myself but they heard Uncle Tony shouting my name.

I was so damn proud. I EARNED some damn respect! I said, *"Thank you."* They extended their hands and introduced themselves. *"I'm Nicky Bigs." "T Money."*

Nicky Bigs was 5'10" or so but he was as wide as a refrigerator. He was wearing work boots and overalls with no shirt. T Money was taller, 6'2" or so and was also massive. He looked to be about 250 lb. I remember he also wore work boots and had a flannel shirt on with the sleeves cut off. His arms were massive and his traps pushed his flannel collar up like nothing I had ever seen before.

"Pleasure to meet you.", I said to both of them. I started to unrack my bar and deep down, I KNEW I was in the right place. Not only was I in theRIGHT place, I was in a SPECIAL place.

I was crushed after that set of squats but I didn't want to leave and I had over an hour before my Dad would arrive to pick me up.

I walked over to the leg presses and loaded five plates on each side. There was a 100 lb plate on each side of the leg press already.

I started with my set and a guy walked up and dropped his gym bag close to the leg press while I was mid set. I felt like I was being watched so I did 20 reps instead of 10. I pulled myself up and he said, *"Mind if I work in, Kid?"*

"Of course", I replied. He dropped into the leg press and banged out his set. His first few sets were slow. He would pause in the bottom and stretch his legs, then lock it out and hold the lock out for a few seconds. After five or six reps he started going slightly faster as he hit 10 more reps with a perfect rhythm.

He pulled himself out of the leg press and stood on the side and said, *"How much ya got, Kid? What's next?"* I asked him to add two more plates to each side. He replied with excitement, *"Well alright!"*

I planned on doing sets of 10 on the leg press but I was now going to avoid anything "normal" at all costs. I got to 10 and grinned out five more reps.

I had gray sweat pants on and my legs were pumped. I could feel and see them stretching against my sweatpants. I got out of the leg press and as I waited for him to tell me how much weight to add, he said to me, "This is good for now, Kid. He introduced himself to me. *"I'm Chucky, what's your name, Kid?"* I replied and he grinned back, *"Good to meet ya, Kid."*

Chucky did 25 reps. I could sense he was not just going to work in with me. He was going to try and beat me. Once I sensed this unspoken competition, I knew it was time to push back and earn more respect, even if it meant being unable to walk or sit on the toilet tomorrow. I didn't care.

Chucky got up from the leg press and smiled as he walked to the side and put his hands on the plates. *"Whaddya got next, Kid?"* I replied, "Let's go with two more plates each side."

'Well alright, Kid!", Chucky replied with excitement. I grabbed a drink from my jug of water. I always carried a gallon jug of water. I saw guys doing it from day one in the late '80s so I started doing it too.

I looked to my left and saw more and more guys coming into the gym. The guy who was playing air guitar was incline dumbbell benching the 180s. I watched from afar as two guys handed him the dumbbells.

Before every set he was crushing the air guitar and air drums. Billy Idol's Rebel Yell was blasting. I dropped down into the leg press and slapped my legs. Chucky had a big smile and shouted, *"Oh yea, now we're working!"* He sat down on the wooden bench that was bolted to the ground, located between the squat racks and the leg press.

Every rep I did, Chucky counted out loud. We were at nine plates on each side and I wanted to get 10 reps but in my mind I knew this would push me to 11 or 12 reps. I got to the 8th rep and my legs were shaking and feeling that deep burn. That burn that causes most to quit.

I put my hands on my legs for a few seconds and shouted *"Two more!"* Chucky replied, *"No way, man! Five more! Let's GO!"*

I grinned and got pissed off. I grabbed the handles of the leg press tightly and HAD to get to 13. After the 12th rep I took a few deep breaths before my final 13th rep. Well, as I was breathing, Chucky yelled, *"Get 20, come on, man!"*

I saw Chucky's grin as he watched me. He was fired up and I was struggling. I got to 17 and I almost got pinned under the machine. My hands let go of the handles and I pushed that rep off with my hands.

I shouted over the music, *"Help me!"* Chucky sat there with a grin and calmly replied, *"Help yourself!"* I got so damn pissed I crushed reps 18, 19 and 20. I racked the weights and the plates rumbled. Chucky laughed and said, "Yea man, that's how you do it!"

I thought to myself, *"Dude, I almost died under that leg press!"* I learned on this very day that Uncle Tony's gym was going to teach me how to transcend every mental barrier and pain barrier I once had.

Chucky told me to take ALL the plates and put them on the leg press. There were twelve 45 lb plates on each side, plus the 100 on each side. Then Chucky said, "Climb on top. I'm gonna f—ing destroy this set!" Chucky had rage in his eyes and I just did as he told me. I weighed 165 or so at the time, maybe 170. Chucky got under the machine and was enraged. He screamed, *"HOW MANY!?"* I said *"Do 20! LET'S F—ING GO!"* Chucky screamed at me, *"F—K YOU, I'LL DO 30!"*

Metallica's song *Battery* began to play. Of course, I saw that guy playing the air guitar nice and slow as the guitar solo began. Then the drums. His arms were flailing everywhere as if he was the conductor of an orchestra. Once the song started to speed up, he grabbed the 100 lb dumbbells and started power curling them.

He would put a slight nudge to curl the weight up and then he would fight the eccentric. Every rep he curled he let out a loud roar, *"Arrrrrrrgggggghhhhh!"*

Chucky started pressing rep after rep. He had a rhythm and would stop every six or seven reps. He would take a few deep breaths and then go again. He got to the 20th rep and his eyes got HUGE. He looked like a madman possessed.

He then hit his last 10 reps non-stop like a piston. When he got to 30 reps he racked the machine and all the plates rumbled. He stood up and I hopped off the machine. When he got up he screamed loudly, *"Wooooooooo!"* I grinned and nodded my head. I realized that I had found my people. I was in a place where everyone could be exactly who they wanted to be and all other things in life happening were left outside these walls.

It was as if there was magic in the air. I felt as if I was developing an alter ego. Like I became someone else on this day. I was stronger than ever before. My pain tolerance went through the roof. It was amazing.

Chucky shook my hands after we stripped down the leg press. He told me to leave four plates on each side. *"If they need anything lighter than four plates, f—k em!"* Chucky laughed after he said that.

Chucky went off to squat which I never saw people do after tough, high rep leg presses. I was going to do some leg curls and leg extensions and then get myself a protein shake from the front desk. Maybe get a little homework in before my Dad came to pick me up.

I would finish with two sets of 20 reps each of leg curls and leg extensions. The music switched to some disco and no one seemed to care. The song *Disco Inferno* came on and the guy who played air guitar was now dancing between sets. It didn't matter what the music or if he was sitting or standing, he was always moving between sets.

As I did my superset of leg curls and leg extensions, this guy was doing the pull over and press with a 45 lb plate on each side. He had a tank top on and you could see his lats, shoulders and arms getting a massive pump.

I was finally done and excited to have earned my protein shake. I saw they were $0.75 and I had plenty of quarters in my gym bag. As I sat down, the song *Rapper's Delight* came on the stereo.

The music guy was actually singing it word for word between sets. He was dancing with himself between sets and pointing at the mirror as if it was the crowd. No one seemed to be shocked by this.

The guy at the front desk introduced himself to me. "I'm Jeff." he said. *"Hi, I'm Zach. Pleasure to meet you."* Jeff went over to a big bucket and put two scoops of protein powder in the blender, some papaya juice and some frozen fruit in the blender.

Jeff blended it up as I pulled out my homework and started getting some work done. Jeff pushed over the protein shake and said, *"Enjoy, Kid."*

I downed that cup of protein and man, it was amazing. Jeff looked at me and said, *"Good!?"* *"Yes"*, I replied. "Can I order another one?" Jeff nodded and made me another shake the same way as I handed him 3 quarters.

I was grinning the whole time I did my math homework. I heard plates clanging and weights slamming, I heard music pumping and guys grunting as they lifted HEAVY and pushed one another.

The dancing guy walked out and lifted his fist in the air. Jeff said, *"See ya tomorrow, George!"* And that was Dancing George. He was about 5'6" and built like a brick sh-t house.

As George left my Dad walked in and waved me over, *"Let's go, Zach!"* We got in the car and my Dad asked me how it was. I told him, *"It was great. I love it here."* He said, *"Good. Good for you."* I stared out the window as we drove home a solid 20 minutes. I couldn't wait for the next training session at Uncle Tony's Gym.

Week after week, month after month I continued to train at Uncle Tony's Highway Gym. I felt bad for my Mom always driving me straight to the gym right after she got home from work so I started to put money in my Mom's wallet without telling her. I always had cash on me from mowing lawns and finding seasonal jobs.

Training at Uncle Tony's Highway Gym was transforming me in more ways than one. I was never a confident kid and every month, I was gaining 5 lb of muscle. The kids at school were starting rumors about me for being on steroids but they had zero clue how hard I was training and how much I was eating.

After every training session Jeff would fix me up with two protein shakes. Jeff would give me basic tips on nutrition and he would always finish his speech with these words, *"Basics for the win, Kid!"*

Jeff had me write down everything I ate for a week in a notebook. He saw my breakfast, lunch, snacks and dinner. Jeff looked at my breakfast and said, *"What's with all the egg whites, Zach? You need some healthy fats. Instead of six egg whites I want you to have 4 - 6 whole eggs for breakfast. You can have toast with butter or some oatmeal with these as well."*

I nodded and listened to Jeff. "For lunch, you need two sandwiches. One sandwich isn't gonna cut it. You're not in the marching band so load up. I want you to mix it up. Tuna sandwiches, turkey, roast beef, PBnJ, these are all good. Anytime you have fish or meat on the sandwich, add some lettuce and tomato."

"Oh yea, drink plenty of chocolate milk. Do they have milk for you at school?" I replied, "Yes, absolutely." "Good. Get whole milk or whole chocolate milk. Skim milk is just water in disguise."

"After school, have a protein shake or any dinner left overs in the fridge. Or, eat something similar to your lunch. The rule I want you to follow is three meals by 3 o'clock. You got it, Zach?" I replied, "Yes, I can do that for sure."

"Ok, then you're gonna lift and get your protein shakes here. When you get home, have dinner. Whatever your Mom makes is good. I see what you've got here and you're lucky. Your Mom cooks plenty of quality food here. I see chicken, beef, soup, potatoes, rice, veggies. This is all good stuff. Then, around 9 o'clock or so, have your last meal of the night. This can be more dinner left overs or anything that resembles what you ate earlier in the day. Breakfast at night is always a good option. So by the end of the night, you've had five meals plus a protein shake. Follow this perfectly and you can expect to gain one lb every week. At your age, your hormones are surging and you can get big just looking at the weights."

It took about three months before anyone at Uncle Tony's gym ever spoke to me let alone acknowledged me minus Jeff and of course, Uncle Tony.

After three months I had gained 17 lb. I looked different and sure as hell felt different. I was confident in myself. My arms, chest, back and traps were stretching through my t-shirts. I wasn't much into fashion so I just bought all the shirts that Uncle Tony was selling at the gym. Uncle Tony would sell clothing from a company called Gorilla Wear. His own shirts and clothing had his logo on it. It was an old photo of Tom Platz squatting with the bar bending.

Uncle Tony must have been friends with Tom because surrounding the mirrors in the gym were countless photos of bodybuilders from the '60s, '70s and '80s. There were a bunch of photos of Uncle Tony with Tom Platz. One of those photos was of Uncle Tony in the squat cage and Tom was screaming at him. The photo always gave me goosebumps. It shouted intensity anytime I looked at that photo.

Other photos around the wall were of bodybuilders and powerlifters. Bodybuilders like Jeff King, Nick Lavitola, Franco Santoriello, Rich Gaspari, Lee Haney, Phil Hill and Johnny Morant.

There were photos of powerlifters as well. I recall seeing these photos and saying to myself, *these guys look like they've been carved from granite.* I saw photos of lifters such as John Kuc, John Cole, Larry Pacifico, Bill Seno, Bill 'Peanuts" West, Bob Young, Doyle Kenady, High Cassidy, Larry Pacifico, Jim Cash and many more. Half of the photos were legends and the other half were men and women who were actual members of the gym.

Seeing all those photos on the walls, my goal was to become someone on that wall. Someone that Uncle Tony respected enough to *earn* my way to the wall. I knew it would not be anytime soon. I knew it would not be months, it would be many years of work ahead of me.

After spending three months at Uncle Tony's I knew I didn't want to leave. I had been to other gyms and I would feel drained the moment I walked in when the music was so low and the radio had commercials on every five minutes.

Have you ever tried squatting your heaviest 5 reps and then some sappy love song comes on the radio? As a teenager, that was a challenge I faced. Learning how to be laser focused regardless of the music. Uncle Tony's Gym was magical to me. When my three month membership ended, I paid for the entire year in full.

The Summer before my junior year in high school I was extremely busy. I would mow lawns every weekend, three lawns on Saturday and three on Sunday. I would get $25 per lawn and sometimes a nice tip.

Twice a week I worked at a pizzeria that my friend convinced me to work at. It was called Casa Giuseppe's pizza and it was right near my high school. My friend told me they needed help, they paid well and I would only have to work one night a week, Friday nights.

Within my first hour I knew this was not the place for me. I was used to manual labor jobs. I had a paper route as a kid and mowing lawns was outdoors with the fresh air. I could work on my tan while mowing lawns and it felt like a constant workout for me. I loved it. Being stuck inside was rough for me. I needed to move and needed fresh air.

After one hour, I was pissed off that my friend convinced me to work here. I couldn't believe he thought I would enjoy this and I learned in that moment to stop saying yes to everyone.

I worked in the back kitchen and I would sweat buckets from the heat. I probably lost 6 lb every Friday working there which was like wrestling practice.

Tony, the owner, was an intense Sicilian. He had a heavy accent and would always curse at me. Every other word from Tony was the F bomb. Abdul was the main cook and Abdul thought it was funny. I remember Tony showed me how to clean the bathroom for the first time. It was my first night working there and every 30 minutes was something new. Cleaning tables, answering phones, taking orders, working the cash register, folding boxes. You name it, I did it.

Tony said to me in his heavy accent, *"Hey kid, get the f—k over here."* I followed Tony to the bathroom and he had a bucket, some bleach and a rag.

He said, *"I want this f-ing bathroom to shine. Look at me. You understand me, Kid. I don't give a f—k. I'll put my hand in the toilet and clean it. That's how you f—ing do it, Kid."*

Tony showed me how to clean the toilet as he grabbed the rag out of the bucket and stuck his hand *in the toilet with no gloves on and then wiped the entire toilet bowl clean with his bare hand and an old rag.*

I was not the type of kid to argue or say no so I did it. I sprayed the toilet with the bleach, grabbed the rag and *cleaned that f—ing toilet.* I was shaking my head the entire time because I was in shock with all the cursing Tony did along with the countless projects he gave me.

After I finished cleaning that *f—ing toilet bowl,* I washed my hands and scrubbed them hard with soap and hot water but I honestly felt like I should stick my hand in a pot of boiling water to really clean my hands. I emptied the bucket and came back to the kitchen.

When I got back to the kitchen, I said, *Tony, what should I do next?* Tony didn't even lift his eyes to look at me. Instead, he was punching and slamming pizza dough on the table like he was trying to murder someone.

He was shouting and cursing about me to Abdul. *This f—ing kid is driving me to the moon. I'm gonna kill this f—ing kid.* I was in shock, I had no clue what was going on. I was cleaning toilets with my hands, folding pizza boxes, cleaning tables, anything he asked me to do, I did it.

Abdul was laughing and I thought to myself, *am I about to go out back and fight Tony right now?* After Tony was done slamming pizza dough and dropping every variation of an F bomb on me, I went out front to pick up the chairs and mop the floor.

One thing I knew how to do was outwork everyone around me. I started recalling a conversation I had with Uncle Tony when I first began training at his gym. Uncle Tony told me, "The greatest respect you can earn is self respect. And the way you get there is by being the hardest worker in the room and not taking shit from anyone."

I kept repeating those words in my head over and over and over again. As I repeated those words, I began to get angry. Angry at myself for allowing Tony to curse at me and put me down. I felt my hands crushing the broom as I swept the floor and I could hear Tony's in the back still cursing about me.

I *knew* that if I kept letting Tony curse at me, that I would regret it all night. I would go home and be unable to fall asleep because Tony was bullying me.

When I was done sweeping, I stood tall and stared back into the kitchen. I could see Tony slamming the pizza dough and punching it over and over.

Abdul saw me staring and my senses perked up. I could sense that Abdul saw I was done with this man cursing at me. Uncle Tony told me *self respect is the most important thing and I would not* let Uncle Tony down. I felt it in my heart and in the pit of my stomach that if I didn't stand up for myself now, then I would never forgive myself.

I must have had a one helluva look on my face because Abdul watched me as I marched past the front counter and into the kitchen. I walked even faster as I passed Abdul and Tony saw me walking in. Tony stopped punching the dough and his eyes opened wide. I caught him by surprise because I am sure he had done this to countless people before. He was a bully and I was about to shut his pie hole and teach him *not to talk down on hardworking people.*

I grabbed his hand and slammed it down on the dough. I had goosebumps and I felt like I would when I was going to squat heavy and destroy anything that stood in my way. Tony was on one side of the table and I was on the other as my hand pinned his hand down. I pressed even harder as he tried to move his hand. I put my body across the table and got in his face and I could literally feel his hand weaken under my hand.

My eyes were face to face with him and his eyes got bigger as he was in shock. I had my teeth clenched and my eyes got big. I could tell that Tony now only saw my rage, he could FEEL it. I had never felt such rage before and I almost didn't know what I was about to do. My teeth clenched and I spoke very slowly to Tony, "You will never curse at me again or I will destroy you." Tony tried to pull his hand away but I was crushing his wrist and I would not let him budge one inch. My eyes were big and I felt possessed. I paused for a few seconds and I'm sure it felt like a lifetime for Tony. "Do you understand me?" I let his hand go and Tony took a step back. I saw the fear and shock in his eyes. I took away all his power. I'm sure he had done this to countless people in his life and I turned the tables on him. I stood there staring at him waiting for him to act or say something. He said nothing and I nodded a few times with a scowl on my face and went back to cleaning.

That's right. I kept cleaning and finished my job. I wanted to let Tony know that I would not be broken by his antics. As I was cleaning, my parents walked in to pick me up and Tony came out to say hello, not knowing this was my parents. He thought they were coming in to order food.

My parents introduced themselves and Tony was in shock. Then, I was in shock. Tony started telling my parents how great of a kid I am and how much he loves having me work at his restaurant. I could not believe what I was hearing and realized I was working for a crazy man.

When I finished cleaning Abdul opened the cash register and paid me. I never said a word to my parents on the ride home and when they asked me how I liked working there, I told them I don't think it's for me and that I'll just keep mowing lawns. As I sat in the back seat telling them my work plans, I had a big grin on my face as I stared out the back window watching the cars pass by. I had been bullied before as a kid and had been intimidated many times in my life. But not this time. This time, I drew a line in the sand and learned what it felt like to have self respect. As Uncle Tony said, *Self Respect is the greatest respect one can earn.*

CHAPTER 4:

WARRIOR MAN
THE ULTIMATE CHAPTER

When I was going through undergrad there was a gym in a neighboring town that I began training out of and eventually got a job working the front desk and doing some private training. My other friends in college were getting jobs like bartending or bouncing at night clubs. I could not see myself doing anything except being in a gym.

The name of this gym was called King's Gym. I came across this gym by accident as I was picking up food for a study group for my Anatomy class and my college professor told me about a local supermarket. When I got to the supermarket, I saw a sign for KING'S GYM on the brick facade outside the building. My interest was piqued and I had to see what kind of gym this was. I parked my car and headed towards King's Gym. As I walked towards the front door that was propped open I could already hear plates rumbling and loud music. As I walked down the stairs there were bodybuilding posters along the entire wall.

There was no one at the front desk and this gym was crowded with equipment further than my eyes could see. King's Gym was narrow but extremely long with high ceilings. The front desk had bodybuilding trophies lined up on the counter and above the refrigerators on a shelf housed all types of protein and energy drinks. I waited awkwardly for a minute to see if someone would attend the front desk, but no luck, so I began to give myself a tour.

It was a Saturday morning around 8 AM and it wasn't too crowded but the lifters in there were working hard. I saw one man training with a woman and more impressive than the guy was this woman. She was jacked! I watched from the corner of my eye as I walked by and she was squatting 315. The gym was lined up one side with endless free weights, benches and squat racks. The other side of the gym was lined up with machines of all types like Hammer Strength and Nautilus. As I began walking back towards the front, the woman was still squatting 315. Her training partner was counting and spotting her and as I walked by he said, "That's 13! Get 2 more!"

I had no clue there was such a serious gym close to my college and I was already planning out my training between classes. I got back to the front desk and turned around to scan the gym again. As I stood there a man walked down the stairs with some bags from the grocery store. He walked behind the front desk and said, "Hey man. How ya doing? I'm Jeff King, let me know if you have any questions or need a protein shake."

I introduced myself and told Jeff that I go to college at Kean University up the street and that I never knew this gym was here. He replied, "Oh yea, we've been here since forever. My Dad used to own the gym. He opened it in the mid '70s and I basically inherited it when he moved to Florida over 10 years ago. I grew up training here!"

I told Jeff, "I'd love to sign up but not today. I've got to pick up a sandwich platter for my study group and get back to them."

Jeff replied, "I'll tell ya what Zach, I might be jumping the gun here but I could use someone like you working the front desk while I'm not here. You're getting a degree in a related field, you're local, and I am always running around with my kids and all their sports." I was excited and without knowing the details I said, "Absolutely, that sounds great!" Jeff gave me his business card, asked for my phone number and told me he'll call me later to discuss the details. Before I left I asked Jeff for a protein shake and he said, "Sure thing, this one is on the house."

Jeff mixed in apple juice, crushed ice, a banana, a scoop of peanut butter and a meal replacement packet from Labrada Nutrition. I insisted on paying but Jeff refused my money and told me to hurry up to my study group and he'll call me later. The protein shake tasted awesome. I hurried over to the supermarket, picked up a sandwich platter for the study group and drove to Kean University.

I was fired up to work at King's Gym. It was a few minutes away and I could make money doing what I loved to do, which was being in a gym. A friend of mine was a waitress nearby and she would work short shifts between classes as well as on Fridays after school. I had the same plan as her even though I had no clue what the schedule might look like or what Jeff had in mind. I was ready before GO!

After studying for 2 hours for a school exam, I drove home and my parents told me there was a voice message on our home's phone answering machine waiting for me. It was from Jeff. He said, "Hey Zach, great meeting you today. I could use somebody here on weeknights and on weekends, both Saturday and Sunday. On weekdays I am looking for 4 PM until 10 PM and on weekends, we're open from 6 AM until 6 PM. The pay is $10 / hr and you can have 2 protein shakes a day as well as train people and keep 65% of the personal training profits. Call me back and let me know if you can start this Monday! Thanks, Zach... talk to you soon!"

I called Jeff immediately and didn't even realize that I'd be working well over 40 hours per week, 7 days a week. I didn't ask about anything because all I could think about was *living* in a gym. Jeff told me to come in on Monday when I was done with my classes and he'll show me how to make protein shakes, how to sign people up for membership, how to answer the phone, my cleaning duties and opening / closing systems.

I was excited beyond my words. On Sunday I meal prepped and packed two Tupperware containers with chicken and rice and planned on making myself one of those shakes that Jeff made me on Saturday morning. During my two classes on Monday all I could think about was working at King's Gym and my leg workout that night.

After class ended I immediately drove to King's Gym and arrived an hour early, it was just shy of 3 PM. I had my gym bag with my gym clothes to change into and my cooler bag for my food. I opened the door and from the top of the stairs I heard loud classic rock. *The Boys are Back in Town* was pumping through the speakers. The energy in this place was awesome. It wasn't that crowded and I knew that gyms don't get busy until about 4 or 5 PM on weekdays.

Jeff shook my hand and he saw I had my gym bag with me. "Great to see you, Zach! Here, take a few shirts and throw one on. When you work here, make sure you're always wearing a KING'S GYM t-shirt." Jeff gave me 5 t-shirts, all of them different colors. The logo was awesome. It was a drawing of the Dave Draper 3/4 back and biceps pose. On the back it said, STRENGTH IS KING. I was proud to wear this shirt and I haven't even put it on!

After I got changed, Jeff had me put my food in the fridge and then he showed me around the gym. There was a closet with cleaning supplies and Jeff said to me, "A hardcore gym does not mean a dirty gym so we keep this place clean. We sell gym towels here and encourage people to use them when they are on benches. Disinfectant spray bottles as you can see are hanging in the front, middle and back of the gym and we tell people to spray and wipe down their equipment as needed. The vacuum and mop should get used either before we open or at the end of the night. This way you're never disturbing someone's workout."

As Jeff walked me through the gym he introduced me to the members and they were all super friendly. There was a family atmosphere at KING'S GYM but you could also sense that it was a place of work. None of the members wanted to converse with me as they were busy training. Jeff brought me behind the front desk and showed me how to work the cash register and reviewed the different things people could purchase at the gym aside from memberships. They sold clothing, protein shakes, gift certificates and personal training packages.

Jeff showed me where to turn the lights on and off when opening and closing and then handed me a set of keys. "I gotta run and take my son to football practice and my daughter to soccer. I'll call the gym later to check in. When you answer the phone, just say *King's Gym, this is Zach, how may I help you?*"

I was kind of in shock at how fast everything happened and there I was, managing a gym with less than 10 minutes of "training." I stood behind the front desk and opened up one of several photo albums. The album I randomly opened was filled with old polaroid photos of bodybuilding and powerlifting photos, all of them from inside KING'S GYM or competing at state and national level competitions.

There were photos of Jeff standing next to his Dad from childhood to adult years. The bodybuilding and powerlifting photos were all super inspiring, some of them I recognized. I saw photos of guys like Jeff King, Nick Lavitola,

Henri Skiba, Louie Simmons, Richie Gaspari, John Kemper, Johnnie Morant and others I didn't recognize. These photo albums were like going through a time machine and I was inspired by every photo.

Every 45 minutes I made sure to walk around the entire gym to organize the weights. I also checked the bathroom and locker room to make sure it was clean. By 5 o'clock the gym started picking up steam as more and more people came through by the minute. Every member had a card and they would place it in a small box alphabetically and I checked each card for the expiration date.

A few of the members introduced themselves to me and welcomed me to "the family". Around 7 PM Jeff called the gym and checked in. He told me that if it quiets down around 8 PM I could train. He also told me to take a few new CDs and change them in the rotating CD player. Between 5 and 8 PM KING'S GYM was packed and I must have made a protein shake every 10 minutes during those 3 hours.

Now I know why Jeff had a fridge loaded with bananas and apple juice. Those protein shakes sold like crazy and the cash register was packed with cash. Jeff stopped by a bit after 8 PM for a few minutes to say, "Hi." Jeff said he would pay me every two weeks as he had one eye scanning the gym floor and told me to train if I wanted to. Jeff shook my hand, emptied the cash register and left in a hurry.

My week was like clockwork. Wake up, eat breakfast, head to school and then run KING'S GYM. Monday through Thursday the gym was packed with powerlifters and bodybuilders from 5 – 8 PM. Friday was not as busy. There were a handful of lifters on Friday and having trained at so many gyms, I knew that Friday through Sunday was only for the serious.

On Friday after 6 PM, there was nobody in KING'S GYM. Jeff stopped in like clockwork to say hello, empty the cash register and then head home to be with his family. Before he left Jeff said to me, "Fridays and the weekends are usually pretty quiet but you never know, sometimes guys train late on Friday's if they finish working their shift as a cop or working at the local Ford plant."

When Jeff left, I looked through the stacks of bodybuilding magazines, some of them dated back to the '50s and '60s. They were *Strength & Health Magazine* and the articles were a blend of weightlifting, bodybuilding, powerlifting and training for athletics. I made myself a protein shake and then vacuumed the entire gym followed by mopping from front to back.

I made sure the floors were devoid of all dust and clean as a whistle. I had an exam the following week so I decided to study for a bit even though it was almost 9 PM at night. I had no problem studying with Def Leppard on the stereo and an empty gym. To me, this was my library. I felt at peace among the **IRON**.

At 9:45 PM I heard loud footsteps coming down the stairs so I stood up. I thought I was either about to get robbed or Jeff was running back because he forgot something. The two guys came up to the desk and they were both MASSIVE. One of the guys had a bandana on and they both had long hair. The taller guy asked me, "When do you guys close?" I replied, "We close at 10 PM." He placed a $100 bill on the counter and said, "I need you to stay open another hour."

They walked to the locker room with gym bags and I called Jeff quickly because I had no clue what to do or who these guys were although they looked familiar. Jeff answered the phone and knew it was me from the caller ID, "What's up, Zach!?"

I said, "Jeff, sorry to call you so late but these two guys came here to train and want me to stay open until 11. Is that OK with you?"

Jeff replied, "Do the guys have long hair? One of them about 6'5"?

Confused, I said "Yes, how did you know?"

He said, "Zach, that's The Ultimate Warrior and Randy Macho Man Savage. They stay at the local hotel when they wrestle at Madison Square Garden. Make them both a protein shake and don't let them pay a dime."

I had to tell Jeff, "The Ultimate Warrior put a $100 bill on the counter."

He replied, "Of course he did, it's yours Zach. Keep it and make sure the music is louder than normal. Warrior Man loves it loud!"

I hung up the phone and 10 seconds later they walked out of the locker room and introduced themselves to me.

"I'm Warrior Man and this is my friend Macho Man. What's your name, Kid?"

I said, "I'm Zach. Pleasure to meet you guys. I'm gonna make you guys a protein shake and leave them right here on the counter."

Warrior Man replied, "That's great, Zach. Can you make Macho Man a cup of coffee? We gotta get the blood flowing for him before we train!"

I went to the office where Jeff had a coffee maker and made a fresh pot of coffee. As the coffee was brewing I watched Warrior Man and Macho Man warming up. Both guys had tank tops on and you could see they were tan, jacked, and ripped! I placed two cups of black coffee on the counter and walked back to let them know the coffee and protein shakes were both ready.

Warrior Man and Macho Man were warming up on a few exercises. I saw Macho Man doing EZ curls on the preacher bench. Warrior Man was pressing an empty barbell overhead, doing both military and behind the neck presses. Macho Man and Warrior Man finished their set and walked to the counter. Both of them slowly sipped on the black coffee and Warrior Man told me to turn up the stereo *full blast.*

After a few sips of coffee, Warrior Man looked at me and said, "Are you just gonna fucking stare at us or do you want to train with!?" I was in shock and taken back for a moment and knew I could not turn down this opportunity, so I replied, "Absolutely. I'll train with you guys!"

I walked to the center of the gym where they were warming up and Warrior Man told me to do presses overhead with the empty bar, then preacher curls and seated overhead dumbbell triceps extensions. It was evident that Warrior Man was organizing the workout and so I followed these guys as they went through the three exercises as a circuit.

After the first round of warm ups, Warrior said to me and Macho Man, "You guys get your own bar for the clean and press. I'm gonna go HEAVY!!!" He screamed at us. When Warrior Man screamed at us, I could tell his alter ego kicked in. I was not a fan of pro wrestling but I saw that this was *not* an act. Warrior Man was about to destroy this place with his intensity.

Warrior Man grabbed a few pairs of 45 lb plates and literally threw them from 10 ft away to land near his barbell. He took a few 25 lb plates and threw them as well. I backed up when he did this to avoid getting destroyed by a plate if it bounced or rolled my feet. Macho Man was very focused on his arm work and seemed like he was going to coast on the clean and press. I had done the clean and press before but not too often. Warrior Man ripped 135 off the ground and pressed it overhead like it was nothing. He would tap the floor gently and then clean and press aggressively every rep, doing 10 reps at 135 for his first set. After 135, Warrior Man added a 25 to each side and then moved on to his preacher curls.

I had my own bar set up as Warrior Man suggested. I asked Macho Man if he wanted to go first and he responded, "Go ahead man, *All You!*" I knew eyes were on me and I had to do this right. My plan was 5 reps so I could go as heavy as possible and not burn out with lighter weights. I was feeling good and did 5 reps.

Macho Man also did 5 reps. When he put the bar down he grinned at me, nodded his head and shouted over the loud music, "Alright, man! Let's do some arms!" We did our preacher curls over the opposite side of the bench which was vertical rather than the angled side. The EZ curl bars were all fixed in KING'S GYM and we started with the 50 lb bar. The rack of EZ curl bars went from 20 lbs all the way up to 150 lb fixed bars. I had never seen anything like them. Macho Man used the same weights I did whereas Warrior Man went *much* heavier, starting with the 100 lb EZ curl bar. These bars were perfectly made from IVANKO. They fit like a glove in your hand as you curled.

After preacher curls, we went to the seated bench and did our overhead dumbbell triceps extensions. Warrior and Macho Man were extremely animated as they trained. They grunted on almost every rep and cheered one another on. I was getting fired up as we had the entire gym to ourselves, the music was blasting and nothing else mattered in that moment.

I started my first set of overhead dumbbell triceps extensions with a 50 lb dumbbell, Macho Man went right after me and Warrior Man started with the 80s. I planned on 10 reps and just as I was going to lap the dumbbell, Warrior Man shouted at me, "Fuck that! Get 5 more, man!" I banged out 5 more and Warrior shouted, "That's how you do it!"

After Macho Man did 15 reps of triceps he stood up and said, "I need some more coffee, man!" Warrior and Macho Man walked to the counter, sipped some coffee, drank some of their protein shake and walked back towards the weights all hyped up. Warrior Man walked towards me while pressing his arms up and down, fingers stretched open as if he was summoning The **IRON** Gods to give him more power as he stormed through the sea of gym equipment. Macho Man marched aggressively behind Warrior Man and looking back, it reminded me of what these men looked like when they stormed out to the ring to wrestle against their opponents.

Warrior Man chalked up his hands and marched directly to his barbell loaded at 185. He squatted down and ripped it off the floor with ease, he took a few deep breaths and pressed it overhead and proceeded to do touch and go reps from the floor to overhead. After his fifth rep he took a few more breaths and then did 3 more powerful reps with 185. Warrior Man's physique was more impressive than any of the bodybuilders I'd seen in person and I had seen countless national level bodybuilders and few pros by this time.

Macho Man and I added a 10 lb plate to each side for our next set of the clean and press. I was fired up and banged out 5 reps with ease. When I finished my set, Warrior Man walked behind the counter and put in a CD. It was Queensryche and the song *"Eyes of a Stranger"* came on first. Warrior ran to the preacher bench just like he was running to the ring. He grabbed the 150 lb EZ curl bar and got right back to work, grunting through every rep of preacher curls. Warrior Man was looking at his biceps and would hold the top of each rep for a solid pause, it was as if he was *willing* his biceps to grow. I could feel his intensity from 10 feet away as Macho Man spotted him and pushed him to get 10 reps.

I didn't want to ask how many sets we were doing or what was next. I wanted to be in the moment as I felt there was no one else on earth having their own weightlifting party on a Friday night! Warrior Man removed the 25s from his bar and literally threw them back towards the plate tree and then slapped on another 45 lb plate, loading his bar to 225. I looked at Macho Man and said, "225?" He shouted back over the music, "Oh Yea!!!!"

Macho Man seemed to be following my lead with the weights we chose so I wanted to see if I could outlift him on at least one exercise. As I did my set of clean and press with 185, Macho Man and Warrior Man would sip their coffee and protein shake between every round of our three exercises. Both of them screamed from across the gym as I pushed for 5 reps. Warrior Man ran back while shouting at me, "Push yourself, Zach!"

My next set of overhead dumbbell triceps extensions was with the 100 lb dumbbell and I got 12 reps. Macho Man stared at the dumbbell for a brief moment as if he was considering going lighter until Warrior Man screamed, "Let's fucking go, Macho Man!" That's all he needed to hear as he grabbed the 100 lb dumbbell, sat down on the bench and ripped it up onto his shoulder and began repping out triceps extensions.

I shouted at Macho Man, "I got 12 reps, you gotta get 12!" Warrior Man shouted, "Fuck that, get 15!" Warrior Man stood behind Macho Man and spotted him as he pushed to get 15 reps, the last three of which were forced reps. Macho Man dumped the 100 lb dumbbell and let out a loud scream followed by a double biceps pose as if he was in the middle of the ring. Macho Man then looked at me and said, "Oh yea, that coffee got me going!"

We all laughed at the same time and I asked Macho Man, "What's next on the clean and press?" Macho Man replied, "Do you remember in the movie Pumping Iron, where Louie is training to beat Arnold? I replied, "Oh yea, I love that movie!" Macho Man replied back, "Me too! I need more weight! I'm gonna beat him! I need 10 lbs on each side." I laughed and got the 10 lb plates and loaded the bar to 205 lbs. As I loaded the bar, Warrior Man loaded his bar to 275 lbs.

The plates were clanging and the music was rockin'. It was the best night I had ever had in my life and I felt like I was living through a movie! Warrior Man asked me, "Zach! Where's the chalk? Do you have any chalk in this gym?" I pointed to the corner where there was a standing chalk bowl welded together. King's Gym was not against chalk or dropping weights. It was a place that was all about hard work and respecting one another and creating an atmosphere that made everyone around you better.

Warrior Man began pacing back and forth near the barbell he loaded to 275 and Macho Man screamed at him, "Let's Go! You wanna slam people! Slam this bar! Pick it up and slam it!" I saw Warrior Man's eyes open up wide as he stared at the barbell for a few seconds and then stormed up to the barbell. Warrior Man squatted down, grabbed the barbell with his massive hands and power cleaned the bar with lightning speed. Warrior Man took a few deep breaths and push pressed 275 over his head. He held it there for a few seconds and then slowly lowered the bar to the front rack position and then dropped it to the floor. Warrior Man took a few deep breaths and did it again. Power. Aggression. Intensity. I didn't know how many reps to expect after the second rep but Warrior Man was undaunted, he attacked that bar one rep at a time until he completed 5 reps of the clean and press with 275 lbs!

After the fifth rep, Warrior Man took his weightlifting belt off and dropped to the floor next to his barbell. It was a special belt made for him from Cardillo Belts. I had never seen a Cardillo belt in person and the only people I saw wearing them were pro bodybuilders. The belt said WARRIOR MAN and you could tell it was not new. This belt had been through the ringer for years and was plenty broken in.

Warrior Man had to get an EZ curl bar that he could load heavier than 150 lbs so I got him the curl bar and he told me to help him put a 45 lb plate and quarters on the curl bar. The curl bar was 25 lbs so the bar was loaded to 165 lb in total. He told Macho Man to hand him the bar after he got set over the preacher bench. Warrior Man's veins were stretching through his shoulders and biceps with a massive pump. Warrior Man banged out 10 perfect reps, each rep looked exactly the same with no fatigue. After 10 reps, Macho Man grabbed the curl bar and Warrior Man told him he's gonna use the same weight for seated overhead triceps extensions.

Macho Man went for more coffee so I had to hand the curl bar to Warrior Man. I carried the curl bar over behind the bench and as Warrior Man sat down and reached his arms back for the hand off, I had to power clean the curl bar off the floor which was extremely awkward but I refused to mess this up. The pressure was on me to be a great training partner and I was NOT going to fail. Warrior Man grunted at the top of every rep of overhead triceps extensions and then he would let the weight slowly stretch before aggressively driving the bar back overhead. After 10 reps Warrior Man shouted, "Two More!" I replied "Alright, I got you, let's go!" After the 12th rep I grabbed the bar from Warrior Man and lowered it to the floor.

Macho Man told me to take the 25s off each side and he and I would use the same weight for both preacher curls and overhead triceps. I struggled a bit on the preacher curls. Macho Man got 10 clean reps and I got stuck mid way through my 8th rep but Warrior Man screamed at me, "Get that fucking weight up!" Warrior Man spotted me ever so slightly to help me push through reps 8, 9 and 10. Macho Man sat down on the triceps bench and I power cleaned the EZ curl bar for him like I did for Warrior Man. Every time I spotted these guys was an added awkward rep of power cleans for me. Macho Man pushed through and got 10 reps and it was my turn.

I began pushing these overhead triceps extensions easier than I thought it would be. By the time I got to 8 reps I decided I would not stop at 10, but instead, I'd be getting 12 reps. I had to beat The Macho Man and I was fired up after struggling on preacher curls. I got to 10 reps and Macho Man tried grabbing the bar but I stopped him, "NO! I'm gonna get two more!" I got my 12th rep and Macho Man took the bar from me. I stood up and hit a double biceps pose while mimicking Lou Ferrigno's Dad from Pumping Iron, "Now look at your arms, Louie." Like you're admiring yourself and you're saying, *"Take a look at this hunk of a man!"*

Warrior Man and Macho Man laughed at me and I could just feel the energy we had going, as if it was enough to light up the entire state of New Jersey. Warrior Man and Macho Man walked to the front desk again to sip some of their coffee and protein shake. They didn't say a word to one another as they rested a bit and caught their breath. I drank from my gallon jug of water and caught my breath while I waited for Macho Man to decide what our last set of clean and press would be.

We stood in the middle of the gym, chalk all over the floor, weights thrown all over the floor from Warrior Man. Here we were, about to plan our final set of clean and press. Warrior Man told me to help him get another plate on the bar for a 315 clean and press. After I helped Warrior Man I said to Macho Man, "Wanna go two plates each side? 225?" Macho Man replied, "Oh yea, let's do this, Zach!" I knew this was going to be a rough set. It was our fifth and final round of work.

Warrior Man began to pace back and forth while staring at the 315 lb barbell. The song "Jesus Christ Pose" from Soundgarden came on and the guitar was blasting through the speakers. Warrior Man stood in front of the barbell and raised his arms to the sky, hands wide open and began pulling his arms down and up as if he was summoning his super powers from The **IRON** Gods. He cinched his belt as tight as possible and squatted down to grab the bar. He rattled the bar by grabbing it viciously and then he ripped the bar up to the rack position. With one quick breath, he dipped down and launched the bar overhead and held it overhead for 5 seconds.

Warrior Man slowly lowered the bar to the rack position and muscled it to the floor. Warrior Man did this for two more reps with the 315 and by the power and control he exhibited, I thought he was going to do five reps. Warrior Man removed his Cardillo weightlifting belt and shouted, "Alright, Men! Now it's your turn!" Macho Man asked to borrow Warrior's belt and Warrior Man nodded in approval. Macho Man locked the belt around his waist as tight as possible and then chalked up his hands.

Macho Man rushed over to the bar and failed his first rep of power cleans! He pulled the bar to about chest height and then dropped the bar. I was in shock and didn't know what to say or do. I went with the tried and true, "You got this!" and Macho Man approached the bar again, this time more methodically. He set up his feet and his stance just right. He took a few deep breaths, squatted down and ripped the bar off the floor to the rack position. Macho Man did a powerful push press and locked the bar overhead for a solid two count. Warrior Man shouted at him, "Two more, Randy! Two more!" Macho Man kept his grip locked on the barbell and performed two more clean reps from ground to overhead.

After his third rep he removed the belt and hit a double bicep, then he kissed each bicep and we all laughed. It was now my turn for the final set of clean and press with 225. With Macho Man hitting 3 reps and Warrior Man 3 reps at 315, I had to finish with 5 reps. I made up my mind and there was no other option in my mind. There would be no easy way out.

I had my own belt, it was a cheap 4" belt I purchased from a previous gym for $16. I put on my belt and locked it up tight as I had never done 5 reps with 225 on the clean and press. I chalked up my hands and then rubbed them together to make the chalk and my hands become one. I visualized myself destroying 225 and moving the bar with speed. In my mind I kept repeating the words, "Speed! Speed! Speed!"

As I approached the bar Warrior Man slapped me on my back and I was NOT at all prepared for that! It actually really pissed me off!! I had to stay focused and locked in. Five reps no matter what! I attacked each rep as if my life depended on it. "Make the rep or die" is what ran through my mind. I could see Macho Man and Warrior Man in slight shock when I was going for more than 3 reps. "Show us what you're made of!!" Warrior Man screamed at me. I got to my fifth rep and held the bar overhead for 5 seconds to show total domination.

Back then I wasn't knowledgeable with regards to proper weightlifting technique so every rep was a muscle clean and a push press. Even though the technique wasn't perfect, this exercise was tremendous for making me feel powerful and building thick muscle on my upper back and shoulders. I remember reading about Arnold performing this exercise when he was at a gym that did not have incline benches. Instead, his gym had standing incline benches so he was required to power clean the barbell to start every rep and then he would carefully step back and lay against the standing incline bench.

Warrior Man and Macho Man complimented my intensity as we took a short rest. Warrior Man said that for our last sets of preacher curls and overhead triceps, we would do a lighter set and get 20 reps of each for the pump. I knew this would be a burner to finish and a real test of pain tolerance. I was used to pushing myself after years of wrestling, training for wrestling and the grueling practices I had been through. Pain was not my enemy, it was my friend and I welcomed the challenge any time, any place.

One after another, all three of us moved through our final arm training like an assembly line. There was no talking. Our intensity did all the talking. No one needed to be motivated or pushed. We had a job to do and we knew what it was. We were like a lumberjack tag team wrecking crew. 20 reps. Period. End of story. They were tough and none of us went with baby weights. The sets of 20 could have easily been stopped around 13 or 14 reps and it was a mental challenge to finish all 20 reps.

I was the last one to finish the workout with overhead triceps extensions. When I finished that last rep I racked my dumbbell and all three of us stood in a small circle as if we were standing around a large fire. Except we were not standing around a fire. We stood around Ivanko plates thrown on the floor, barbells loaded to 225 and 315 and chalk mixed with sweat all over the area we trained in.

Warrior Man said, "This was the BEST training session I have ever had on the road! Thank you, Zach." Macho Man thanked me and walked up to me with his arm extended. I went to shake his hand but instead his hand grabbed my forearm and we shook arms, embracing like ancient gladiators. Macho Man looked me in the eyes with a grin as we embraced one another's arm. Warrior Man approached me and did the same, embracing my arm like a gladiator. His hand was massive and literally wrapped around my forearm.

I told the guys to go finish their protein shakes and I'll clean up. Warrior Man told Macho Man to meet him at the front desk. Warrior Man told me he wanted to help me clean up. Macho Man stepped behind the counter and lowered the volume of the stereo so we could barely hear the music. As Warrior Man returned the plates I grabbed the mop and bucket and cleaned the entire floor and made it look as if no one was ever there. The floor was spotless and clean.

Warrior Man walked back to the counter with me and said, "Let's eat and rest. We need to fuel up for tomorrow." At the counter Warrior Man placed two cans of tuna on the counter as did Macho Man. I asked them if they had anything else to eat besides tuna and they both told me this is how they eat on the road, lots of tuna and water. I offered them some carbs as I had two Tupperware containers with chicken and rice. Their eyes opened and they were excited and both said "Absolutely, that would be great!" As I heated up my food, they both ate their tuna from the can after draining them in the sink. We had paper plates in the office so I put the rice on two plates and ate a double serving of chicken. I had 4 chicken breasts in one sitting and was starving after that intense training session.

After we ate, I cleaned off the counter and then they asked for me to call a cab for them but I told them I would drive them to their hotel. As we left KING'S GYM I felt a wave of gratitude come over me as I knew this was the right place for me. I was lucky. I didn't find this gym, it *found me*. As I drove back to the hotel Macho Man fell asleep 1 minute into the ride while in the back seat. Warrior Man said to me, "I don't sleep much on the road, I don't know how Randy does it. I envy how easily he falls asleep. When we get to the hotel I'll drop off my bag and we can take a walk if you want, Zach."

I replied to Warrior Man, "Absolutely, if you're not too tired." Warrior Man said to me, "Zach, I won't fall asleep until about midnight or 1 AM and then I'll be up before 5 AM." I pulled up to the front of the hotel and Warrior Man opened the back door to wake up Macho Man who was stunned when he woke up. "We're here already!?! Hey, Zach. Thanks for the ride and the great training session. We'll see you again, real soon, buddy." Warrior Man said to me before closing the trunk, "Zach, park your car and meet me in the lobby. I'll be down in 3 minutes."

I parked and waited for Warrior Man in the lobby. The temperature was perfect as it was late Spring and here I was, waiting for Warrior Man who wanted to take a walk. It was all surreal that I had just trained with two of the biggest celebrities in the world yet when we trained together, we were all equals. I had always felt this about the gym but I had never trained with celebrities or famous people so the context was extremely powerful.

After a few minutes, Warrior Man walked through the lobby and signed what seemed like 20 autographs, signing photographs and t-shirts. Warrior Man nodded to me that we should begin walking and we walked out of the hotel. Warrior Man asked me where there's a quiet place to walk and I told him we could cut through the hotel parking lot and walk a few blocks away to some quiet neighborhoods. He nodded and said, "Alright, let's get out of here for a bit."

As we walked away from the hotel and left towards the nearby quiet neighborhoods Warrior Man said to me, "Listen, Zach, I normally don't get in such great workouts when I'm on the road and that means a lot to me that you stayed open for us and trained with us. Randy was exhausted and ready to go to the hotel but I told him we had to train. We drove down from Boston and last night we actually slept in our cars after wrestling in front of 15,000 people."

I said, "Holy shit that's crazy, why did you guys sleep in your cars?" Warrior replied, "Zach, this business will destroy you and run you into the ground if you let it. You must be extremely disciplined with your money and your body. Your body is your business card. Most of all, you must stay disciplined with your mind or you'll end up disabled or dead from this business. Guys end up spending all their money on fancy hotels, fancy living and all sorts of drugs. Eventually, I'll be done with wrestling and I want to be able to move on in my life but only on my Own Terms, not when Vince or someone else tells me to do so."

We walked a bit more and I soaked in the words of Warrior Man. I didn't know what to say as he was confiding in me and seemed to need a kindred spirit to speak with. Before I could respond, Warrior Man said to me, "Man, how awesome was that training session!? I love training with that kind of intensity. Most guys can't train like that anymore. They do all kinds of light pump up training. In wrestling, you need to be strong to perform the moves and stay healthy. I've always used the clean and press because I knew it was going to help me lift the big guys. Without strength I'd have to change my style of wrestling and that's just not what I'm about."

I said to Warrior, "I love training that way, too. It's been a while since I've had training partners so I got fired up working with you guys." Warrior Man asked me, "What are you gonna do with your college degree? I was neck deep in Chiropractic School back in the day but my bodybuilding success caught the eye of some pro wrestling recruiters and that led me to pro wrestling."

I told Warrior Man I was planning on finishing college and getting a teaching / coaching job after college but want to pursue my PhD and eventually teach in college. Warrior Man calmly said, "I like that you have a plan but hear me out on this, Zach. Make sure you can always write your own paycheck. What I mean by that is never rely on one source of income. I've owned a gym before, I sell my art work and also consult with high level businessmen. The key is you can always walk away from anything that doesn't sit right with your heart. It's Not what you can say yes to, it's the freedom to say *Fuck You* to anything and anyone that doesn't line up with your values."

That advice really hit home for me in that moment. As we continued to walk through the quiet night, Warrior Man said to me, "This walk reminds me of Arizona. I've got a million dollar home in Arizona but when I get home from life on the road, I don't sleep in the house. I take a long walk through the desert and meditate as I walk through the night. A lot of people don't know this but Warrior IS my legal name. I changed it because Warrior is not an act for me, it's who I am whether the face paint is on or not, whether I am wrestling or not. When I walk through the desert, the javelinas, scorpions and hyenas would follow me but they never came within 20 ft of me. I would sleep on the desert floor, under the stars and moon and become one with the desert, the darkness and the stars. I believe within all of us, there is Genius. You must *never* let anyone *squander* your genius. The schools and people in general will try to tell you how to think, what job to get, and to be more practical. Fuck that and fuck them." We walked a bit more and it was getting close to midnight when I checked my watch. I asked Warrior Man, "Let me know when you need to head back to get some sleep."

Warrior said, "Zach, listen to me..... You were put on this earth for something bigger. You were put on this earth to be GREAT. If you've got a fire burning inside of you to do something then make sure you pay attention to that. Answer the call. If you try to put out the fire by ignoring the flame, you will regret it for a lifetime."

I replied, "Warrior, I gotta tell ya, all I think about is training. I want to build a place that is more than a gym. I want to create something that inspires people to live a STRONG life beyond the weights. I know that training and bodybuilding changed my life and without the gym, I really don't know where I would be right now. I want to create something that empowers people."

Warrior man replied, "Then that's what you need to do, Zach. Answer your calling. Find a way to make it happen. Looks like you're on the right path by working at KING'S GYM."

I replied, "Ironically, I just started working there and I found it by accident." Warrior Man said, "Maybe it's the other way around. Maybe KING'S GYM found you!"

When we got back to the hotel the lobby was empty. It was just shy of 1 AM. Warrior Man told me to wait in the lobby as he was going to his room to get me something. Warrior Man came down 5 minutes later with a book and said "Let's sit down for a minute, Zach. I want you to have this book but I want to sign it for you."

We sat at a table and Warrior Man opened the book. The book was small and it was titled An Iron Will by Orison Swett Marden. Warrior Man opened the front cover and paused in deep thought for about 10 seconds before he began to write. After he closed the book we both stood up and he went to shake my hand but like we did at the gym, we embraced arms like ancient Gladiators. Warrior Man said to me after we embraced arms, "Zach, I want you to do what you were put on this earth to do. Never forget... You were put on this earth to be GREAT. I left my address and home phone number in the book as well. Let's stay in touch. Always Believe!"

Warrior Man hugged me and handed me the book and left the hotel lobby and headed to his room. I felt a pit in my stomach after Warrior Man walked away. I was a bit sad not knowing when or if I would ever see him again. It was late but I wasn't tired at all. My mind was racing about *Why was I put on this earth!?* I decided to sit down and see what Warrior Man wrote for me in the book. I opened the first page and saw the note Warrior Man wrote to me.

Zach,
You must show no mercy...
nor have any belief whatsoever
in how others judge you...
for your greatness will silence them all."
—WARRIOR

I read that note over and over for what seemed like 20 minutes. I flipped through the pages of An Iron Will and found a piece of paper folded up in the middle. I don't think Warrior Man realized he left this paper in the book. I opened it up and read what seemed to be something Warrior was working on. Perhaps it was a book of his own?

Here's what it said.....

"Every man's heart one day beats its final beat, his lungs breathe their final breath and if what that man did in his life makes the blood pulse through the body of others, and makes them bleed deeper than something larger than life, then his essence, his spirit, will be immortalized by the storytellers, by the loyalty, by the memory of those who honor him and make the running the man did live forever."

—*The Ultimate Warrior*

When I read that letter, it gave me goosebumps. I began to cry and I wasn't sure why I was crying. I could feel the intensity and passion that came from Warrior's words. I could hear his voice as I read that note. It was now time to take my OWN passion and intensity and fulfill my destiny on this earth.

And if you so choose, it is also Your Time. It is up to YOU.

Live The Code 365,

Zach Even-Esh

Zach Even - Esh

Printed in Great Britain
by Amazon